PROBLEMS OF THE AGED

PROBLEMS OF THE AGED

Compiled by

CLYDE B. VEDDER, Ph.D.

Professor, Department of Sociology and Anthropology
Northern Illinois University
DeKalb, Illinois

and

ANNETTE S. LEFKOWITZ, Ph.D.

Professor and Head
Department of Nursing Education
Northern Illinois University
DeKalb, Illinois

CHARLES C THOMAS · PUBLISHER
Springfield · Illinois · U.S.A.

Published and Distributed Throughout the World by
CHARLES C THOMAS • PUBLISHER
BANNERSTONE HOUSE
301-327 East Lawrence Avenue, Springfield, Illinois, U.S.A.
NATCHEZ PLANTATION HOUSE
735 North Atlantic Boulevard, Fort Lauderdale, Florida, U.S.A.

© *1965, by* CHARLES C THOMAS • PUBLISHER
Library of Congress Catalog Card Number: 64-24060

With **THOMAS BOOKS** *careful attention is given to all details of manufactur-
ing and design. It is the Publisher's desire to present books that are satisfactory
as to their physical qualities and artistic possibilities and appropriate for their
particular use.* **THOMAS BOOKS** *will be true to those laws of quality that
assure a good name and good will.*

Printed in the United States of America
N-1

AUTHORS

ANNIS, EDWARD R., M.D.
President
American Medical Association

ANSART, MANUEL BASTOS, M.D.
Professor of Surgery
University of Barcelona
Barcelona, Spain

ARNOLD, EDWIN T., Jr., M.D.
Hogansville, Georgia

BEATTY, KATHRYN ANN
Institute of Gerontology
Mt. Angel College
Mt. Angel, Oregon

BRACELAND, FRANCIS J., M.D.
Psychiatrist-in-Chief
The Institute of Living
Hartford, Connecticut
Former Past President
American Psychiatrac Association

BRECHER, EDWARD

BRECHER, RUTH

CHARLES, DON C.
Professor of Psychology
Iowa State University of Science and Technology
Ames, Iowa

COVALT, NILA KIRKPATRICK, M.D., F.A.C.P.
Medical Director
Kirkpatrick Memorial Institute of
Physical Medicine and Rehabilitation
Winter Park, Flordia

v

Authors

GILBERTSEN, VICTOR A., M.D.
Minneapolis, Minnesota

HALE, MARK P.
Director
The Jane Addams Graduate School of Social Work
University of Illinois
Urbana, Illinois

HENLEY, BARBARA M.
Research Social Worker
Comprehensive Care and Teaching Program
The New York Hospital—Cornell Medical Center
New York, New York

HORWITT, M. K., Ph.D.
Director
L. B. Mendel Research Laboratory
Elgin State Hospital, Elgin, Illinois
Associate Professor
Department of Biological Chemistry
University of Illinois College of Medicine
Chicago, Illinois

LONERGAN, ROBERT C., M.D.
Formerly Associate Professor
Northwestern University Medical School
Chicago, Illinois
Former Medical Director of the
American Legion Hospital for Crippled Children

ROSSI, LAWRENCE J., M.D.
Medical Director
Hopedale Hospital
Hopedale, Illinois

SAGAL, ZACHARY, M.D.
Formerly Assistant Clinical Professor of Medicine
New York University

SCHWARTZ, DORIS, M.A.
Instructor in Outpatient Nursing
Cornell University—New York Hospital School of Nursing
Coordinator
Comprehensive Care and Teaching Program
Cornell University Medical College
New York, New York

SHAPERA, RICHARD P., M.D.
Clinical Instructor in Medicine
University of Pittsburgh School of Medicine
Medical Advisory Committee
Harmarville Rehabilitation Center
Senior Assistant
Medical Staff, Montefiore Hospital
Pittsburgh, Pennsylvania

SHEELEY, WILLIAM F., M.D.
Chief of the American Psychiatric Association
General Practitioner Education Project
Washington, D.C.

SILVERBLATT, MARVIN L., M.D.
Clinical Instructor in Medicine
University of Pittsburgh School of Medicine
Associate, Medical Staff
Montefiore Hospital, Pittsburgh, Pennsylvania

SOMMER, ROBERT, Ph.D.
Associate Professor
University of California
Department of Psychology
Davis, California

SPARKS, S. L.
Administrator
Schlesinger's Home
Beaumont, Texas

WANGENSTEEN, OWEN H., M.D., F.A.C.S.
Minneapolis, Minnesota

WHITEHOUSE, FREDERICK A., Ed.D.
Director of Rehabilitation
American Heart Association
Fellow, American Psychological Association,
the American Public Health Association,
and the American Association for the Advancement of Science
Member of the Medical Committee of the
President's Committee on Employment of the Physically Handicapped

PREFACE

Glib catch phrases have been bestowed upon many facets of our social existence. There have been "Lost Generations," "Beat Generations" and behaviors which have been described as "Golden Age," "Age of Reason," "Renaissance" and the like. Today we face in this "Atomic Age" a problem which defies the definition of our era. There has never been such a concentration of elder citizens since the chronicles of man.

The increasing growth of the older population is a matter of concern to those interested in the problems of the aging. Considerable progress has been made in the technique of population projection, but the projections still rest on assumptions as to future trends in fertility and mortality. The demographer hasn't had much more success in prediction than has the stockmarket forecaster or the meteorologist forecasting the weather.

Between 1900 and 1950 the total population of the United States increased by nearly 100 per cent, from about 76 million to 151 million. In the same time period, the population 65 years of age and over increased by nearly 500 per cent, from 3.1 million to 12.3 million. These figures then indicate how our population has "aged" in the first half of the 20th Century.

There are several reasons to explain this social phenomenon which has kept sixteen million people alive beyond the age of sixty-five by 1960, compared to around three millions alive at age sixty-five at the beginning of this century. Probably most important, this increase in the aged populations is due to the saving of the lives of infants. Most of the individuals in our population over sixty-five were born after 1860. Prior to 1860 the birth and death rates in the United States were relatively high. The death rate was reduced by shifting from the rural- agrarian to the urban-industrial way of life. Important changes took place in medical knowledge, science, sanitation, and modes of living. Millions of young adult immigrants found their way to our shores. The combination of these factors accounts for the disproportionate increase of the aged population over the total population.

It is past time for society to recognize that old age does not have to be measured chronologically, or by the accident of birth in a particular year. All old people are not white-haired, wrinkled, slovenly in dress, bent and sickly. Physiological, intellectual, and sociological ages should be considered as well as the chronological age.

Until recent years, research among the aged tended to be limited to the sick and institutionalized. Spurious generalizations were frequently made from studies of economically or physically defeated older people. Such generalizations have led to serious flaws in social planning and thinking, since the vast majority of the aged in our society are relatively healthy and do not fit in to the commonly fallacious thinking.

Despite this new "image" of the aged, personal and social problems still abound. Many people refer to old age as an "age-old Problem." Old age may always have been a personal problem, but old age has only become a social problem very recently and the existence of millions of elderly people in the United States is a new phenomenon. People are living longer, the old are getting older. This gift of longevity is a mixed blessing to millions who have reached the age of sixty-five and over. To overcome various problems that face the aged, education, work, family life, recreation and social services will have to be revolutionized. As Natalie Harris Cabot has indicated, when retirement age is reached, the family grown, the friends dispersed, and financial resources become limited, the question, "What shall I do today?" may become the most challenging issue of the mid-century.

The aged are regarded differently from those in the younger age brackets. The more heterogenous the population, the more difficult it becomes to generalize. In the United States the aged constitute one of the most heterogeneous of all social categories. Modern industrial societies pose problems for the aged that would not obtain in agrarian groups. The aged in our society become a problem because of the type of society in which they live. There is a premium on youth and a liability on old age. The aged have a few adult roles to play and are frequently made to feel useless and unwanted. Modern society has few status positions for the aged to fill and for the status positions there are available, the supply far exceeds the demand.

Much of the security which the family formerly provided for the aged is now supplied by the state. Old age and survivor's government pensions insure against want and illness, but there is a rising curve of physical and mental illness in the later years of life. More favorable life-expectancy is offset by fear of disabilities peculiar to the aged.

The aged rely less upon the family than before, since the former moral and legal obligation of economic support by children no longer obtains. Sons and daughters are not apt to offer a home to widowed parents. Children are more apt to shift the medical care of aged parents to some hospital rather than to provide a bed in their home. The aged must look elsewhere than to their progeny for companionship and sociability. To satisfy financial, health and social needs, the aged today turns to government and other organizations. Much housing designed for the elderly residents is subsidized by national, state, or municipal governments.

The high mobility of modern society leads to the dispersal not only of relatives but of friends. It is difficult for the aged to make new friends. They are deprived of the society of their family, and having lost associates on the job and friends by death or departure to other communities, find themselves with too much time on their hands. In this roleless role, the aged begin to think of themselves as being "put out to pasture," or "up on the shelf," or just "watching the world go by."

Milton L. Barron has characterized our older citizens as a minority group since they suffer from certain discrimination as do racial and ethnic groups. In a sense, they are second-class citizens and may be deprived of their full rights to economic, social and civic participation. Conditions making for frustration and anxieties such as retirement fears, deprivations of status, insufficient income, anxiety about persistent illness, and economic inflation tend to threaten the positive mental health of a sizable proportion of older people.

The over 65 face special problems not met by young people such as senility and arteriosclerosis, which do not yield to treatment. James E. Birren quotes from a California survey of 1952 that the most frequent mentioned unmet needs of persons at or beyond the retirement age were medical care and drugs. Also found was an expressed need for such items of health maintenance as dentures, eyeglasses, hearing aids, and hospital care. It is difficult for many of the aged to present a picture of well-being to society. The likelihood of an increasing number of unmet needs is an added burden of social indignities to many an aged individual.

The opportunities for continued active participation in civic, business, political and social affairs as a means of fulfilling adult roles by the aged diminish rapidly as one nears retirement age. Contemporary society faces the task of finding for the aged generation new solutions for conditions that, up to now, seem to defy substantial improvement.

CONTENTS

Contents

PROBLEMS OF THE AGED

SENIOR CITIZEN AT THE CROSSROADS*

M EN OR WOMEN in their later years soon learn from radio, TV or newspapers that their problems—the problems of aging— are now a major concern not only to themselves and their families but to their physicians, the hospitals, and other taxpayers.

The senior citizen is confronted with a steady stream of complicated and confusing information related to his health, housing and the way in which he spends his time and money. Solutions given for his problems often seem vague, complex and faraway— that is, until lately.

HE NEEDS MORE FACTS

Just recently he may have received a letter from his congressman, who wants to know if the senior citizen favors an addition of health insurance to his Social Security benefits. If he carries Blue Cross or Blue Shield he is likely to receive a notice of some change in the premium or benefits (in an increasing number of areas, senior citizens find that now they can enroll after 65).

By now newspaper-advertisement coupons have probably been read which offer hospitalization benefits for six dollars a month; or hospitalization with other considerable benefits, including nursing-home-care expense, for $8.50 a month. Both of these policies are limited with exclusions, but they are available to all over sixty-five without physical examination, and for small monthly premiums.

In any case, all the senior citizen must do is sign his name. If he applies for voluntary insurance, or keeps what he has, he pays for it. He can sign now in favor of government insurance at no

*What's New, 213:3-8, 1959. Courtesy of Abbott Laboratories.

cost to him; and he may surmise that any possible benefits he might receive from it won't cost *him* anything, now that he's retired. Moreover, he could drop any voluntary insurance he carries, and inflation is causing him to drop more and more of his accustomed expenditures every day. He has seen or heard both adverse and glowing accounts of the effects of socialized medicine in other countries, but he has almost no facts on which to base his decision.

More than anything else, his decision is apt to depend largely on the community in which he lives—and whether or not it affords him and his problems of aging an "honest, undecorated respect."[2]

Approximately two thirds of all persons sixty-five or over in the United States now live in urban communities.[3] "The old man who formerly aged happily and gracefully on his farm often finds himself in a city trying to live in a poor apartment on less money than he needs to meet a bare standard of living; thirty years ago, if he worked for a company, he could stay on as long as he could do his work well; today he is deprived of his job at sixty-five, medical science has lengthened his years . . . he must go on living . . . he must eat and keep a roof over his head."[4]

According to Vogt,[4] the percentage of employed men past sixty-five dropped from 68 in 1890 to 42 per cent in 1950, and today only 25 per cent of both sexes are gainfully employed after sixty-five. He reports a nationwide survey which shows that 36 per cent of those over sixty-five haven't enough income to meet a minimum budget, and 53 per cent have less than enough for a self-respecting standard of living. The average monthly Social Security payment is $64; the 1958 average for new O.A.S.I. enrollees was $74.47. The April, 1956, Social Security Bulletin reported $2294 as the median income of families with the head of the household over sixty-five, and $796 for those of that age living alone. Almost half of these families and about 85 per cent of those living alone had annual incomes under $2000.[5] "Today's estimate is $2500 per couple and $1230 per individual."[6]

HOW MUCH MONEY CAN HE SAVE?

Are Americans provident during their earning years? In 1955, about 9 per cent of all Americans had annual incomes under

$2000; 48 per cent had less than $5000. In 1957, a fourth of all Americans had no *cash* savings; more than half had less than $500; and less than a fourth had $2000 or more.[5] It would seem that about 75 per cent of Americans are unprepared for a major medical or hospital expense, some of them not even for minor ones without adequate health insurance.

About two out of three Americans do have some type of prepaid plan for hospital care, but two out of three have no medical expense coverage, and 70 million lack surgical insurance. About one in three have no hospitalization insurance of any kind. Among those without health insurance are two thirds of all families with annual incomes under $2000; three fourths of those employed on farms; and about half of those past sixty-five.[5] Obviously, not only the aged but all Americans might profit from clear-cut, understandable information on adequate health insurance, if it were properly presented.

On the other hand, the cost of adequate health insurance, including medical, surgical, hospital or nursing-home care, may seem, and indeed may be, beyond the means of the senior citizen, if he has not secured it through job-retirement benefits; and it is difficult to estimate how much the cost of insurance can be lowered for the rapidly increasing numbers of elderly people, and have it remain actuarially sound. In many cases, physicians are setting their fees for those past sixty-five in accord with today's economic realities, but high hospital and nursing-home rates are almost prohibitive to many, and are still rising.

Everywhere there is the immediate and paramount necessity for the citizens in each community to provide those facilities which will maintain the health of their senior citizens and enable them to remain at home as long as possible. The aged prefer to remain at home, and they will put up with considerable inconvenience and deprivation to retain their independence. At present it is estimated that only 5 to 6 per cent of the 15.2 million Americans past sixty-five are in institutions, and that possibly 2 per cent more of the four million at home with some chronic disability may need some type of institutional care.[6,7]

HIS HEALTH AND HIS TIME

In New York City. Some communities, and some groups of individuals, provide facilities which encourage and help older people to maintain their health, independence and well being. Rusk[8] observes: "I think we in medicine have done a particularly good job with our own retirement problems . . . now we must apply social and psychological tools to the emotional necessities of our patients . . . I'll give you an illustration.

"Fourteen years ago in the Bronx, welfare workers couldn't get their work done because there was a constant stream of old people coming by all day with some kind of complaint. Finally one worker said, 'I don't think these people have anything to complain about; they just don't have any place to go.' . . . So they furnished three rooms in an abandoned city hall with an old piano, pool table and card tables . . . Five years later the club they set up for these old people had 700 members, aged sixty-five to ninety-six (with an average age of 76). They had shops, a weekly dance, and a monthly play written by an eighty-one-year-old playwright. There had been eleven weddings. When the senior-center group was compared with a similar one of the same age and socio-economic level, they had 50 per cent less hospital admission for physical illness, and their visits to physicians and clinics had dropped 50 per cent.

"The American Psychiatric Society estimated an expected forty psychotic breaks requiring admission to a mental institution in such a group over a five-year period. The records failed to show any admissions for senile psychosis. Had there been eight such breaks a year, for five years, the government cost for their care would have been $10,000 more a year than was spent to run the center for the 700.

"Three years after the fourteenth senior center was opened in New York City, in a Puerto Rican Harlem district, there had been only two such breaks among the 400 members there, though they represented twenty-six nationalities and ethnic origins."[8]

In San Francisco. A visitor entering the San Francisco senior center is taken by surprise. As he steps directly from the city street into a huge, circular glass-walled room, on the edge of San Francisco bay, the wide panorama of blue water and passing ships, blue skies and distant hills seems to be a part of the room in which he stands. This "Bay View Room" in city-owned Aquatic Park was opened as a drop-in senior center in 1948, because so many old people were seen sitting idly all day in the city's hotels, stores, YMCA or parks.

"But we learned from older people," says Miss Vickery,[9] the director of the center, "a senior center should not be a program already planned and directed by well-meaning people who want to help old people have a good time. Membership responsibilities are the key to the successful senior center; and this is quite different from attending activities. Old people do not want to be forced into dependent positions; their struggle for independence persists. They need to feel worthwhile, to be needed and useful, and to possess dignity. And we have learned that older people can develop new skills and social insights; they can play new roles and carry new responsibilities.

"Each member should carry some responsibility for the program, if possible, make some financial contribution toward it; each should contribute something of his abilities and skills. Our members learn to teach, and to lead; teachers are brought in only when needed skills are not to be found among the members. The membership carries on some twenty-five different activities and community service projects. This has great significance for them and gives them deep satisfactions.

"Our counselor is available when needed to help with personal, health or housing problems of members, or to allay those tensions which are inevitable among those working or playing in groups. All members are encouraged; here the mind can reach toward new horizons, and the hand toward new skills.

"Members come to the center through publicity about it in the newspaper, or on TV or radio; through referral by a physician, nurse, social worker, another member, or a younger individual in the senior citizen's family. Often the younger relative comes to investigate the center before recommending it to an older family member. Later we may get a report that the almost intolerable tensions that had arisen with three-generation living have eased or disappeared when the older relative has a life of his own with his contemporaries."

The older person takes the first step to solve his problem of aloneness when he comes to the center. Here a hostess welcomes him, and he sees a counselor who determines what responsibility he could take for the program. He is given a guest card and invited to visit the center three times before he decides on becoming a member. A hostess keeps in touch with him, and at the third visit the counselor sees him again before he makes the decision.

A balance is kept in the membership between those who are more alert and able, and those who are frail or handicapped. The more alert and able members teach and aid the others to make friends, and to develop new interests and the desire to assume some responsibility, however small, for the program. In this way those who are timid, handicapped or less alert come to be accepted by all.

Members who become homebound are brought to the center by the Red Cross once a month for a homebound party. Each member brings his own sandwiches; the center provides dessert and coffee. For some this is their only opportunity to eat with others. Absent members are called, and ill or injured members are visited, if they desire it.

Average monthly dues are 50 cents; some can pay 25 cents because many of the engineers, nurses, teachers, public employees, artisans, clerical workers or other members had retired before Social Security went into effect, and they have very modest or low incomes. But the membership, in cooperation with the board, conducted three money-making events for the year 1957-1958. The remainder of the annual budget was met by gifts from foundations, individuals, or corporations; by the United Community Fund, and the San Francisco Recreation and Park Department. (The center is open for eight hours on four days a week, for ten hours on two days a week, and closed on Saturday. In 1957-1958, the total daily attendance was 29,371; the average monthly attendance was 2448.)

A training program at the center provides experience, observation and instruction to professional or volunteer leaders who work with older people at other centers in the city elsewhere.

Members of the San Francisco senior center are *involved in* and are responsible for a program that has become a community asset. They are doing something which interests them and at the same time avoiding the senile depression that comes from being alone; both physical and mental health are benefited.[9]

In Detroit. The Kundig senior center in Detroit[11] furnishes another kind of service that holds much promise for the aged who need a therapeutic, semiprotective environment to enable them to remain in the community. Their members are aided in securing suitable rooms within walking distance of the center. They accept all races and creeds, and many of their fifty-four members have minimum incomes from old age assistance or Social Security, and cannot maintain themselves at home. They spend their days at the center where they receive nutritious meals, health supervision, recreation and companionship with their own age group. All have as much independence as they can manage, and as much protection as is suitable for their conditions.

In addition to the staff, a public health nurse is at the center two hours a week where she spends most of her time in health counseling. Poor eating patterns of the aged are a constant problem, and she encourages the correction of dental defects and poor dental hygiene. A public health nutritionist serves as consultant.

A physician acts as volunteer medical consultant and usually makes at least two calls a month. He examines those without medical care, and strongly advises the others to continue their previous medical management. Chest x-rays are taken on admittance and yearly thereafter through public health services.

Occasionally, a member may be ill at home, and the nurse or city physician may see him there. If he needs hospital services he receives them at a hospital which has some support from the United Community Fund. Medical records at the center accompany the member to the hospital, and the nurse requests hospital records for the center when he returns. All services to members are noted on regular visiting nurse association morbidity records.

Ideally, all applicants for this type of service should be examined for physical, emotional and social states of health to determine if they need this type of environment, and that it fits their needs.[10]

Some homes for the aged, to be discussed in following articles, offer similar day care to selected individuals.

In Suburban Menlo Park, California.[11] The outstanding senior center in the United States is not in a congested big city, but in a town where it might appear that specialized services for older people would not be used to any extent. "Little House" at Menlo Park is in an area which has been characterized as residential, white collar, middle class, with a substantial proportion of youthful population made up principally of commuters. Nearby Stanford University is the dominating cultural influence in the community.

But in 1947, some 175 women living there organized a group called the Peninsula Volunteers, Inc., or the PVs, in order to foster projects of community interest and welfare. And in 1948, physicians, educators and other interested persons suggested that the PVs investigate problems of aging. They found that services for older people were greatly neglected by communities, and selected gerontology as their major interest.

In 1949, the PVs rented a little house in the center of town near shopping and transportation facilities, and offered opportunities for community service and instruction in simple crafts to all over fifty years, regardless of their color, race, creed or place of residence. In a year they were forced to move to larger quarters, which soon became inadequate; they asked the city to help them secure a well-located site for permanent quarters. After legal obstacles were overcome, the city allocated about an acre in a corner of centrally located park, and the PVs assumed the financial responsibility for the building and program.

PV members, interested friends and foundations, and Little House members raised $80,000. A building designed to meet the special needs of older people was completed, dedicated to senior citizens, and deeded to the city in 1954. The PVs lease the building from the city for a dollar a month, and maintain the interior; the city maintains the exterior, landscaping and grounds.

Since the center opened, two additions have increased the total floor space to about 10,000 square feet and the total building investment to $125,000.

Today, Little House has the appearance of a large ranch-type home, set in a well-tended lawn with borders of brightly colored flowers. On a much used patio, senior citizens relax in lightweight, "non-tip" furniture, or play cards and shuffleboard. Nearby there is croquet, bocci ball or horseshoes. Nowhere are there steps or raised thresholds to obstruct anyone with failing eyesight, or those who use a cane, crutch or wheelchair.

Inside, large windows everywhere admit abundant light needed by aging eyes of members who work in craft rooms, lapidary or woodworking shops; who read or study in the library; or who prepare food in the kitchen. Comfort, convenience and safety are provided here and in the conference room, TV-lounge, two large meeting rooms, halls and offices. There have been only a few accidents at Little House.

Physicians, educators, business men and other interested citizens, with the PV Board of Directors and director of Little House, make up the advisory board which determines the policy for the center. Financial support comes from a shop operated and owned by the PVs, the PVs' annual fund-raising event, friends, foundations' the annual fund-raising bazaar and contributions of Little House members.

Little House has self-government through a council which represents the members in each department. About thirty PVs serve on the committees in each department as advisors, and they cooperate with the director and members in carrying out the program. There is nothing haphazard about the management of Little House; its affairs are carried on systematically as in any membership organization.

A new member may be welcomed first into a group where activities include teas, card-playing, dancing, croquet, shuffleboard, horseshoes, or trips to important events or points of interest. This stimulates interest in most of the participants for beginner classes in creative arts, and later in more advanced courses, drama, the chorus, lectures, discussion groups, or nutrition. Usual-

ly the interest continues to adult education offered at the local
high school and colleges; often this provides a new means for
full or part-time employment.[11]

Others, like Margit Sediansky, may begin their reorientation
into their proper places in community life through a generous gift
of a special talent. Recently, she gave brilliant interpretations of
Liszt's Hungarian Rhapsodies, Beethoven's Moonlight Sonata,
Chopin's Polonaise, and parts of Verdi's Rigoletto for members
of Little House. It was easy for her audience to understand that
the polished performance they heard came from a former pianist
of a world-famous Budapest orchestra in Hungary and a teacher at
National Music School at Szombathely; but it was difficult for
them to realize that when the concert was over, the sixty-seven-
year-old, gray-haired pianist would return as cook and companion
to a family which has given her refuge, a job and the privilege of
practice on a piano.

Only Margit Sediansky could explain it: "Twice I fly the Com-
munists; twice I must leave my piano, my books and clothes."[12]
Many who heard the concert at Little House hoped and believed
that it was a beginning of her way back to her career of artist and
teacher, and her appropriate place in her new-found community.

Community service is an important part in the lives of Little
House members. These senior citizens have a deep sense of loyalty
and service to each other; and they respond readily to appeals for
service in their community. Little House has become an important
two-way street in Menlo Park, and a busy one.

Aided by a professional dietitian employed at Little House,
members cook and serve a sixty-cent lunch on five days a week
for those who make reservations. Some members who live at a distance or without cooking facilities find the service invaluable.
They get one nutritious meal a day and companionship while eating. Members issue and mail a free *News Letter* every month to
the entire membership. They visit the ill and homebound, and
help each other informally in many ways. Some members make
special equipment for the handicapped in clinics; others work the
year round on articles for the annual fund-raising bazaar.

PVs with special training counsel members on problems of
housing or employment. They conduct a clinic for the local busi-

ness men and chamber of commerce, where employers find new employees. The director of Little House, a professional social worker, counsels members who have other personal problems. She knows all of the community resources, and refers those in need of specialized services to appropriate agencies. A government representative calls regularly to advise on retirement insurance. Recently, Little House members heard a distinguished physician speak on developments in management of heart disease.

Membership at Little House seems to have stabilized around 1250; about thirty-five members are lost each month through death, moving away, or a change in the life of the older person which relieves him of a need for the services at the center; about thirty-five new members are enrolled every month. The average monthly attendance is now 4000.

The sponsoring PVs stress the small beginning of their service and demonstration project, and its gradual development. They find that a community will incorporate special services for its aging citizens, if educated to the need for them.

Since Little House was opened senior centers and organized activity programs have been established in five neighboring towns. A countywide committee on aging has developed from a four-year study on mental health. This year the Ford Foundation allocated $50,000 jointly to the PVs and Stanford University for a three-year research program of evaluation of the Little House project. Stanford University School of Medicine is revising its curriculum to put new emphasis upon socioeconomic studies[11] and phases of gerontology.

A California Citizens Advisory Committee on Aging, composed of four legislators and eight citizens, studies problems of aging; recommends appropriate measures to the governor; acts as an information and clearing center; and assists local committees throughout the state to develop their own senior citizen activity program. A member of PVs serves on this committee. California has some 100 senior citizen programs.[1]

Experience has shown that the senior citizen will accept the information he needs to help him maintain his health and independence in a senior activity program, and in the comfortable setting of the senior center. If properly organized and conducted the senior center is a valuable community resource for the physician who treats older patients.

REFERENCES

1. KUPLAN, L.: *Geriatics, 13:*808-814, December 1958, and personal communications.
2. SULLIVAN, H. S.: *The Psychiatric Interview.* W. W. Norton & Co., Inc., 1954, page xxiii.
3. KAPLAIN, J., AND TAIETZ, P.: *Geriatrics, 13:*752-757, November 1958.
4. ALVAREZ, W. C.: *Geriatrics, 13:*25A-30A, December 1958.
5. McGUINNESS, A. C.: *Southern Med. J., 51:*1537-1540, December 1958.
6. Report of Special Committee on Aging, California Medical Association. *California Medicine, 90:*291-293, April 1959.
7. ABBE, L.M.: Special Staff on Aging, U. S. Department of Health, Education and Welfare, personal communications.
8. RUSK, H. A.: American Academy of General Practice. *GP, 18:* 163-167, December 1958.
9. VICKERY, F., Executive Director, San Francisco Senior Center: Personal communications and reports.
10. OWEN, R. E., *et al.*: *Amer. J. of Nursing, 58:*1676-1678, December 1958.
11. RUSSELL, A. M. G., PVI: E. Stetler, Director, Little House, personal communications; Report to California Advisory Committee on Aging September, 1958. *Aging,* No. 34, U. S. Department of Health, Education and Welfare, August 1957.
12. ZOBEL, L.: Penisula Living *Palo Alto Times,* April 11-12, 1959. p. 15.

OUTSTANDING CHARACTERISTICS OF OLDER PATIENTS*

Don C. Charles

Is THERE ANY REASON for treating older patients differently from middle-aged or younger ones, other than those reasons dictated by specific illness or disability? Obviously, the older patient *is* different, simply by virtue of his having lived a great many years, of having an aged body, of having left most of his peers behind.

He may, however, be quite unwilling or unable to accept these differences himself. Some years ago, I inquired of a colleague of retirement age, "When did you first begin to feel old?" At first, he looked puzzled and then annoyed as he snapped, "I haven't ever felt that way yet!" I was young and naive and would know better now than to ask the question.

Yet it was not many months later that the same man complained to me that he was old, that nobody wanted him around, that he wasn't any good for anything. Which of his protestations should I have believed? Actually, both statements were accurate. The second one was made after he had retired and had suffered a serious illness.

These responses suggest something of the degree to which health and the immediate environmental situation affect the older person. Having relatively little time left to live, he often finds it difficult to take a long and hopeful view when misfortune—illness, accident, loss of loved ones—strikes him.

To the young person the elderly patient's tenuous hold on life may suggest that he has little to live for. I remember the surprise—and faint disapproval—in the voice of a young woman when she

*American Journal of Nursing, 61:80-83, Nov. 1961.

told of asking a nice, white-haired old lady in confidence at what age women ceased being physically interested in men. "You'll have to ask someone older than I, my dear," was the reply.

Old people *are* different from young ones, and thus they do require different care. But, like young people, they are still individuals with needs and desires and with some of the means for satisfying them. Knowing some of the ways in which older patients differ from younger ones in their physiological and psychological functioning may be helpful. Following are some of the most noteworthy age changes and some suggestions for helping patients adapt to them.[1]

SENSORY AND PERCEPTUAL FUNCTIONS

We are constantly bombarded by stimuli of many sorts: noises, lights, colors, odors. Our sense organs—eyes, ears, nose, skin, inner ears—detect these stimuli and transmit impulses to the appropriate brain centers for interpretation. The latter process of getting meaning out of experience is what the psychologist calls perception. As people age, the efficiency of both the information-gathering and information-interpreting functions declines somewhat.

Vision. Some age changes are well known: the decline of acuity, speed of focusing, and accommodation in near-point vision. Less familiar, perhaps, is the fact that breadth of the field of vision narrows several degrees from middle to old age. The matter of light and vision is of practical concern to the nurse. With increasing age, adaptation to darkness deteriorates.

Thus, it is most important that older patients not be faced with the necessity of going from lighted rooms into dark hallways, bathrooms, and the like. High levels of illumination are needed for tasks which demand good acuity—craft work or reading, for example. Each thirteen-year age increase requires approximately doubled light intensity.

This combination of narrowed field, slower perception, reduced acuity, and need for high illumination suggests that elderly

---

[1]For a comprehensive evaluation of research evidence on the psychological aspects of aging see *Handbook of Aging and the Individual,* ed. by James E. Birren. Chicago, University of Chicago Press, 1960.

ambulant patients need careful supervision, especially at dusk or at night, if they are to get about safely.

Auditory Perception. While everyone suffers some high-frequency hearing loss in the adult years, most people retain fairly good hearing for speech sounds throughout life. However, with age there is increasing incidence of deafness in the sound range of the human voice. After age seventy-five, about two men out of every ten, and one woman out of ten, suffer from noticeable deafness. The result is increased difficulty in hearing speech.

Patients are sometimes unaware that they are not perceiving accurately some vowels or consonants or are unwilling to admit their lack of understanding. Therefore, the nurse, as a matter of course, should speak slowly, enunciate clearly, and check to see if she is being understood, especially when instructions for medication or self-care are being given.

Even the presence of a hearing aid is no guarantee of hearing. It may be turned off, intentionally or unintentionally, or it may be malfunctioning. I know one elderly, deaf woman who habitually keeps wornout batteries in her instrument, saving her good set for church and special social occasions.

Body Perception. By this I mean an awareness of the body's position, its status, and functioning. There is a steady loss of pain sensitivity after the age of fifty. This might seem at first to be a good thing, and indeed, some elderly people apparently do not suffer as much as their disorders would suggest.

However, loss of pain sensitivity is dangerous. Older people, without apparent awareness, not uncommonly suffer fractures, bruises, or other damage to the body, which should have medical attention. The nurse needs to keep alert for symptoms of such damage, even though she has no report of an accident.

There is some loss of kinesthesia, perception of movement of body parts. Of greater concern is the loss of sense of balance, apparently owing to changes in the inner ear. Many of the falls suffered by elderly people are not a product alone of weakness or poor muscular control, but a lack of awareness that the body is off balance until it is too late to recover.

For this reason, even patients who are not particularly feeble need stair and hallway railings, grips by the tub, and other appropriate supports. Some will require canes or a nurse's guiding arm.

The loss of ability to adapt quickly to temperature changes is well known. Older people thrive on a constant temperature and require frequent changes of covers or wraps when the temperature fluctuates.

MOTOR SKILLS

In discussing motor performance, we must consider several processes: sensing and decision-making in the brain and central nervous system, and responding.

Sensory functions were discussed previously. Decline of muscular strength is continuous after the twenties. It is selective. Loss of back strength, for example, occurs early and is quite rapid, while good hand strength is retained into quite old age. Accompanying the decline of strength is decline in capacity for continuous exertion, necessitating more attention to rest periods to avoid excessive fatigue. The implications for convalescent patients and those undergoing occupational therapy are obvious.

The general slowing down of responses in older people is familiar to all of us. While some slowing occurs in the peripheral (sensory and muscular) apparatus, the significant change occurs in the central nervous system. Thus, it is not sensing or responding that is so difficult for aged people, but rather *deciding how to respond.*

This is especially marked in complex performances, in unfamiliar tasks, and where the stimuli are presented too rapidly or in an irregular fashion. Apparently, there is a tendency to overlap the organization of one act or movement with the previous one, resulting in jerky and piecemeal performance.

To get the most efficient motor functioning from the older patient, therefore, one must structure the situation so there is sufficient time for planning in his central nervous system. This may be accomplished by presenting instruction or information slowly, allowing time for him to get set, by using rhythmic stimuli when possible, and especially by avoiding hurried, confused, or emotion-laden orders.

It is interesting to note that motor functioning in familiar tasks declines little, if at all, provided that the skills have been exercised regularly. The older person may steer an automobile, knit, or repair a watch as efficiently as he did two or three decades earlier, while a less difficult but new task may be done clumsily and inefficiently.

LEARNING ABILITY

Most nurses are teachers, although they may not think of themselves in this way. Some—certain public health nurses, for instance —teach in formal training situations. Most of the nurse's teaching, however, takes place incidentally as she goes about her duties in the sick room and the ward. Old patients have a great deal of learning to do—learning to master new prosthetic appliances, learning to approach familiar tasks in new ways as heart, limbs, or muscles fail to respond as they once did.

The nurse is likely to be the professional person in most intimate and frequent contact with the elderly patient as he attempts to acquire these new skills. Even more difficult is his need to learn new understanding of himself, to change his attitudes toward many things. Thus the nurse needs an answer to the familiar question, "Can you teach an old dog new tricks?"

Research evidence suggests that the most appropriate answer to this question is, "Yes, if you have the time to teach him and he has the desire to learn." In other words, old people still learn, but the importance of time, teaching techniques, and motivation increases with age.

It was once supposed that intelligence reached a peak in the teens and thereafter declined steadily and with an increasing rate. Current evidence to the contrary suggests that at least some people continue improving in ability into middle age and perhaps beyond. Unquestionably, however, the older person does differ from a younger one in his learning characteristics. His loss in speed has been alluded to earlier. This is only one facet of his learning behavior, of course.

To say that he becomes less efficient is true, but only partially so. His loss is relatively slight in areas which are familiar through his everyday experience. However, he becomes steadily less efficient as materials become less familiar, and he will be markedly inefficient if he is forced to reorganize old familiar material in new and strange ways.

His memory, too, deteriorates. Here again, old and often-repeated material is retained at a relatively good level, but new and especially strange and unfamiliar material is lost readily. Thus, an elderly woman may remember the details of a recipe used for her daughter's wedding cake many years ago but becomes hopelessly confused about the name of a drug prescribed for her or about the name of a disorder her physician mentioned.

Another well-known characteristic of the thinking process of old people is rigidity. Tasks requiring quick changes of "set"—expectation or readiness to respond in a certain way—are usually not performed well. Under stress, the older person tends to repeat himself even though it is apparent to himself as well as others that what he is doing isn't working. He may even regress to a bit of behavior that was successful in the past.

In the little country town where I grew up, there were still a few older farmers driving horses when I was a child. I remember the account of one, reluctantly converted to an automobile, shouting. "Whoa! Whoa!" and pulling of the steering wheel as he crashed through a store front.

Deterioration in the organizing function of the brain leads to some failures in logical thinking. When pressed to solve too-difficult problems, the older person is likely to retreat into discussion of extraneous material rather than provide logical inferences from evidence.

Perhaps it should be noted at this point that the discussion of deterioration refers to ways in which persons become less efficient in their learning and reasoning as they grow older. One should not infer that all old people are rigid, illogical, forgetful, and so on. There are tremendous differences in individuals in rate of deterioration, and, obviously, current level of functioning is relative to the original peak level.

There is at least one psychologist, for example, who is producing stimulating and scholarly books although he is past ninety. I have no doubt that he functioned more efficiently in the 1890's when he took his doctor of philosophy degree than he does today, but his work is currently more creditable than that of many younger men in the field.

Most older persons, unlike the scholar just mentioned, are not high achievers. There is a tendency to sit back, to relax, to let things go as they will. Too, physiological conditions may affect drive or ambition. For whatever reason, a major problem with older learners is motivation. Before learning can occur, there must be some desire to learn, some perception of reward for making the effort.

The nurse who is trying to help elderly patients acquire new ways will have to be skillful in making learning seem intrinsically rewarding and satisfying. Praise, recognition of even a little progress, encouragement, and patience are essential.

To summarize teaching techniques with older patients:

1) Use every motivating device at your disposal; praise and recognition are of greatest importance.
2) Keep materials in the context of the familiar as much as possible. Relate new experiences or materials to familiar ones, especially in the early stages of learning.
3) Assume that a great deal of time will be spent in any learning situation. Never give the impression of pushing or hurrying the learner, regardless of your own need to get the job done.
4) Help the patient understand the task; he may be unable to perceive the relation of parts of the task to the whole.
5) Keep stimulus and response together when demonstrating or explaining.

ADJUSTMENT

It would be unrealistic to attempt to treat the broad topic of adjustment of aged people in so brief a space as this. There are, however, some points that should be noted.

In general, the adjustment of healthy individuals resembles their adjustment at an earlier period of life. Behavior is relatively consistent over a period of time for reasons of both genetic and environmental continuity. However, there is a continuing loss of life-enjoyment, of feelings of self-confidence and usefulness, and a general loss of zest.

There is, in addition, a loss of what might be called resiliency. Stress of any kind causes more anxiety and elicits a greater reaction than was true at an earlier age, and recovery is slower. The youthful person generally expects to recover from illness or disability, to be as good as new again. The aged person is only being realistic when he recognizes that he won't be new again.

One frequent manifestation of this realization is hypochondriasis. In many older persons, normal aches and pains are magnified, excessive attention is directed to digestive and eliminative functioning, and exaggerated reports of sleeplessness are made. Most of us know inactive older persons who nap happily in the daytime and then complain bitterly of sleepless nights. Only time for acquaintance and familiarity will enable the nurse to distinguish which symptoms have an organic basis, which are serious, and which trivial. The family's reports are not always reliable, either.

The real adjustment problem of age lies in apathy and futile resignation. One bit of evidence of this is the close relationship between age and suicide. But depression does not need to proceed to the extreme of suicide to be harmful to the patient. Loss of the will to live can be as fatal psychologically and physically as more direct forms of self-destruction.

Obviously, formal psychotherapy with neurotic or depressed patients is not considered the forte of the nurse. She may, however, play a role in prevention. Both overconcern with bodily health and a loss of will to live may be aggravated or even instituted by a common condition—boredom. There is accumulating evidence that deprivation of stimulation, literally from birth to old age, is a cause of psychological malfunctioning.

It is highly desirable that old people experience as stimulating an atmosphere as possible and that they continue to do as many things as their condition allows. It is especially important to keep this need in mind when caring for patients in nursing homes or in working with those who are chronically ill and bedfast.

Elderly men and women, with all their crotchets, can be rewarding patients. Their philosophies occasional wry humor, and accounts of their experiences are often enjoyable to the listener. By keeping in mind their psychological needs and capacities, the nurse will help them retain dignity and self-respect. She will encourage them to use and, thus, to maintain their remaining skills and abilities. Her reward will be not only a virtuous feeling of altruism, but the satisfaction of pleasanter and more cooperative behavior in patients.

PROBLEMS OF THE AGING*

IF THE RECOMMENDATIONS from the White House Conference on Aging are put into effect, there'll be an increasing amount of government participation—federal, state, and local—in solving the problems of the aged. The need for an expansion and extension of funds, research, personnel, and programs in this area was stressed in almost all conference reports.

The purpose of the conference, held January 9 to 12 in Washington, D.C., was to spell out the needs and problems of the 50 million Americans who are forty-five and older, to formulate general policies, and recommend specific actions to meet those needs. An official conference report from Washington D.C., will be made in April.

Of the 2700 delegates attending, the majority were appointed by governors and 695 represented 308 national organizations, including the American Nurses' Association and the National League for Nursing.

It is believed that conference findings and recommendations will be widely used in the coming years as a guide to actions in the field of aging by states, communities, the federal government, private organizations, and older people themselves.

As LeRoy Burney, former surgeon general, U.S. Public Health Service, said, no conference brings a "sudden meshing of all gears," but the White House Conference on Aging can be considered a success if a coordinated effort to provide service for the aging develops, and people can say, "This movement started rolling after the White House conference."

*American Journal of Nursing, 61:55-57, March 1961.

For conference purposes, the whole field of aging was arbitrarily divided into twenty subject areas, each assigned to a section ranging in size from seventy-five to 400 delegates. The sections organized and correlated conference recommendations and drafted policy statements concerning their own subjects.

Among those covered were: population trends, income maintenance including financing medical care, employment security and retirement, health and medical care, rehabilitation, the role and training of professional personnel, local community and state organization, national voluntary services and service organizations, and federal organizations and programs.

At the opening session, President Dwight D. Eisenhower said, "I hope that out of your deliberations will come recommendations that Congress can use later in its own deliberations." Two days after the conference, Senator Pat McNamara, Democrat, of Michigan, introduced a resolution in Congress for a special committee to study the findings of the conference.

Major controversy during the session was on financing health services for the aged with the final recommendation calling for health insurance for the aged under the social security system.

Section 2 on Income Maintenance had jurisdiction to make recommendations on this subject. Section 20 on Federal Organizations endorsed the social security approach to financing health services for the aged and Section 5 on Health and Medical Care condemned it, but former Representative Robert W. Kean, Republican, of New Jersey, chairman of the conference, ruled both of these sections out of order.

It was reported that about 180 of the 280 doctors attending the conference were in the Health and Medical Care Section which was chaired by Leonard Larson, president-elect of the American Medical Association. Before this section was ruled out of order, members voted 165 to 122 to condemn the inclusion of health care benefits under social security.

There is little doubt that the majority of the conference delegates endorsed the financing of health care under social security. In a plenary session, the entire assembly indicated overwhelmingly that it did not wish to vote on the question but preferred the recommendations to come from Section 2.

The final recommendation reads:

Private voluntary effort and public assistance can contribute much to the solution of the problem of health care for the aged. However, they will continue to fall short of meeting the basic medical care needs of the aged as a whole. The majority of the delegates of Section 2 (by a vote of 170 to 99) believe that the social security mechanism should be the basic means of financing health care for the aged.

Among the speakers who urged this action were Marion B. Folsom, former Secretary of Health, Education, and Welfare, and Arthur Larsen, of Duke University, former director of the U.S. Information Agency, former Under Secretary of Labor, and special assistant to President Eisenhower.

Speaking before the section on federal organizations, Mr. Folsom said that administering health insurance for retired people through social security was "the logical plan, the one which is endorsed by most students of the subject." He pointed out that a small tax of from 0.25 to 0.5 per cent on the payroll of each employer and employee would finance a reasonable plan "without adverse effect on the federal budget and with little if any adverse effect on the economy."

He found no basis for labeling such a plan "socialized medicine." "The individual would still have the same free choice as to hospitals and doctors that he now has."

Among other conference recommendations on social security benefits and old age assistance were:

● The earnings test should be retained in social security but should be modified. (Now a retired worker whose salary is more that $1500 annually is penalized financially.)

● The present $4800 base for computing Old Age Survivors and Disability Insurance taxes and benefit should be increased periodically as wages rise.

● Women should be eligible for old age assistance at the age of sixty-two instead of sixty-five as they are now.

● Residence requirements for old age assistance should be abolished.

Several section reports urged the expansion and improvement

of pension programs. Among actions recommended were the expansion of tax incentives to encourage private savings and pension plan development and inclusion of vesting provisions in pension plans so that workers who change jobs can retain some retirement benefits. Reports also pointed out that one of the more acute problems that can be remedied through changes in existing employer and union policies is compulsory retirement at an arbitrarily set age.

Dwight S. Sargent, personnel director of the Consolidated Edison Company of New York and chairman of the planning committee for Employment Security and Retirement for the White House Conference, pointed out that:

> Somewhere between a third and a fourth of American workers have employers with pension plans, but according to some estimates, upwards of half of them never qualify for pensions, and even today, only about a million and a half American workers are actually receiving private pensions. One of the big reasons is that many of the plans have no provisions for "vesting" or guaranteeing pension rights for workers who lose or quit their jobs, or for accumulating credits for service with a succession of employers, as now occurs under the Old Age and Survivors Insurance program.

In the report from the section on rehabilitation a number of statements could affect nursing and nursing education. In urging the expansion and improvement of rehabilitation services the report stated: "Rehabilitation services could well be a condition of accreditation for hospitals, particularly those with approved internship training programs."

This report also pointed out that qualified teachers must be provided and well structured units for the teaching of rehabilitation principles are needed in schools of medicine, dentistry, nursing, and related disciplines.

If present population trends continue, Howard A. Rusk, chairman of physical medicine and rehabilitation at New York University College of Medicine, said that, "In twenty years, every able bodied worker in the United States will be carrying one disabled worker or one person over sixty-five on his back."

The section on health and medical care reported that special emphasis needs to be given to strengthening and greatly extending services for the care of older persons at home. Since this would require additional financing, it was recommended that federal and state agencies "seed money" to encourage communities to experiment with ways of providing care for elderly patients at home. It was pointed out that prepayment and public assistance programs should make specific provision for payment for services in the home. "The crucial role of nursing services in chronic illness requires specific provision of payment for such care," the report stated.

In discussing mental health needs of older people, the report stressed the importance of certain positive concepts. Among them were: that mentally ill aged persons should receive service from the same agencies serving other groups, that the aged should receive mental hospital service only when they are mentally ill; if commitment is indicated, plans should be started immediately toward return of the patient to the community; plans providing health care should not exclude the mentally ill.

NEED FOR PROFESSIONAL PERSONNEL

The section on the role and training of professional personnel said professional organizations, appropriate government units, and other groups should see that undergraduate, graduate, and professional education includes "appropriate content on aging in a form similar and equivalent to other knowledge about man and society." It was further recommended that "specialization in aging within appropriate disciplines and fields through the addition of specialized courses, research opportunities, clinical and field experiences" be expedited.

Increased numbers of trained professional, technical, and related personnel in all fields concerned with meeting needs of older persons was called urgent as was the rapid and thorough increase in the number of faculty equipped for teaching in aging within the biological and social sciences and within the professional curriculums in all health fields. Financial support from all levels of government as well as foundations, business, labor, and private and voluntary groups would be necessary to achieve this, it was stated.

Other conference recommendations called for the establishment of committees or agencies to promote and coordinate services for the aging at local, state and national levels, including an institute of aging within the National Institutes of Health.

HELPING THE ELDERLY FIND
COMMUNITY SERVICES*

Barbara M. Henley

EVERY NURSE KNOWS a "poor old Mr. M"—or someone like him. He appears in the clinic, his bewhiskered, gnarled old face lighting up with a vague, pleased smile when someone speaks to him. His walk is hesitant, his grasp unfirm, and frequently he breaks or forgets his appointments.

And then there is Mrs. R, sixtyish, resolutely groomed, loud voiced, officious, and querulous. She dislikes to be kept waiting. She asks for innumerable small favors. Her eagerness for attention is pathetic. Her demands irritate personnel and fellow patients alike.

Mrs. R and Mr. M. appeared in a study conducted during the last four years at New York Hospital-Cornell University Medical School—a study of Nursing and Psychosocial Needs of Elderly Patients.[1] For a description of the study of chronically ill patients attending a medical clinic, two articles are available (1,2). The complete study will be published in the spring by the Macmillan Company.

Although the 220 patients studied were city dwellers, predominantly immigrants or first generation Americans with a very high incidence of chronic illness, there is evidence that their problems are representative of low-income, noninstitutionalized old people in the general population.

*American Journal of Nursing, 63:4:89-92, April 1963.

[1]This study was financed by the Nursing Resources Division of the U. S. Public Health Service and was conducted with a randomly drawn 10 per cent sample of the elderly clinic population.

Patients like Mrs. R and Mr. M are in trouble. But multiple social services are growing up to meet their needs, particularly since the White House Conference on Aging in 1961. The social worker and the nurse, who have contacts with such patients, should be aware of these new services. Both must work with, refer, and inform elderly patients who need such help.

The social worker in her traditional function uses knowledge and skill in community action, group work, and casework. It is in the latter role that she and the nurse are most likely to share responsibility for patients. As community services become more complex, a kind of exercise in the use of them has grown up. The social worker knows not only what is new in rapidly expanding services, but she knows what kinds of individuals are motivated to use the help. She knows not only the procedures for applications and the size of waiting lists for services, but she can evaluate how to time the referral so that the individual client's strengths are most fully utilized. All social workers are trained to act as integrators or coordinators of community services. Where social workers are not available, resourceful nurses may have to include part of this coordinating function besides their responsibility as referring agents.

Nurses are in a unique position to detect the problems of the elderly. Some evidence indicates that the public are more ready to tell their troubles to the familiar person of the nurse than to the more distant, more "specialized" person of the doctor or the social worker (3). Nurses must be aware of existing services for older people, and make themselves sensitive to the unspoken needs of their patients in order to be able to refer them where they can secure help.

A brief overview of recent advances in community services for the aged is presented here. A good text on geriatric nursing can provide information in depth about the wide variety of facilities (4).

Some of the most recent services augmented here are fairly widespread, some are still in the vanguard. Unfortunately, even in this wealthy nation, welfare standards vary greatly from state to state. By and large, services lag behind knowledge about needs.

LIVING ARRANGEMENTS

Recognition grows that there are alternatives to institutionalizing unprotected or chronically ill older persons. Visiting nurses have enabled thousands of them to stay in their own homes. Today, many other community agencies help older persons remain in the community. Frequently both homemaker and housekeeping help may be secured. Individualized shopping help can sometimes be arranged. In about eleven major cities, some provision is made for distributing at least one hot meal a day to homebound patients (5).

The trend toward helping older patients become self-reliant is reflected in the growth of facilities designed for the aged by federal, state, local, and private sponsors. The Housing Act of 1956—broadened in 1959 and 1960—liberalized financing for private rental housing and for home purchases for elderly persons. Some states require that a portion of all state-aided, low-rent, public housing units be specifically designed and reserved for aged persons.

Accommodations for older persons vary—furnished and unfurnished apartments with kitchenette or without, cottages, or dormitories. Some communities set aside portions of housing units for elderly tenants to allow different generations to live together. Sometimes residential settings have special recreation facilities for older citizen—cafeterias, infirmary care, optional maid services, and other built-in conveniences. Two noteworthy examples (and there are numerous others) are the Mayflower Home in Grinnell, Iowa, and Willamette View Manor in Portland, Oregon.

Some departments of public welfare and family services agencies administer special boarding arrangements or foster homes for the elderly. Such arrangements assure supervision and help if needed, and one hopes, in addition, the warmth of a shared household. An interesting phenomenon of late is the Adult Counselors and Home Finders in New York City, a private, fee-charging organization, run by social workers, who have made a specialty of locating highly specialized living arrangements in the community for the elderly people of *all* classes and needs.

Finally, no discussion of living arrangements for older persons would be complete without mentioning organized home care. Many an aged invalid has been helped to maintain something like business-as-usual through medical services at home provided by a local institution.

TIME AND MONEY

One solution to problems which can accompany retirement, but not an easy one, is to help oldsters remain at work or find more protected job settings or shorter hours of work. In the recent past, both voluntary agencies and local branches of the United States Employment Service have started using special counselors for elderly job applicants. Their services include aptitude testing, retraining, aggressive job seeking, and community education.

The Senior Personnel Employment Committee in White Plains, New York, and Program for the Aging, Committee on Employment, of the United Community Fund of San Francisco, California, are attempting to change the apathy and prejudice of local employers through enlisting the cooperation of community leaders and businessmen. They are primarily staffed by volunteers.

By and large, there is some pessimism about the feasibility of wide-scale employment of the elderly in other than marginal positions at marginal salaries. Counseling and planning for retirement *before* retirement would seem to be the most realistic long-range solution. In some communities, small business loans, sheltered workshops, and opportunities for work at home are feasible.

Old people, free from the pressures of work and child rearing, need more from their spare time than an occasional change of scene, a holiday treat, or infrequent company. We realize increasingly how enormous the problem of unoccupied time is. It affects every area of the old person's adjustment and has implications for his total health and well-being.

The old-age center—broader in its outlook than clubs for older people—is relatively new. Such centers offer a program of services in a specially designed facility where old persons meet regularly under professional guidance. A recent survey located 218 centers in thirty-one states offering, solely or in combination, such services as recreation and education, drop-in centers, information and referral centers, and direct services for individual problems (6). The

best of them stress enhancement of the physical, social, and emotional well-being of the oldster.

It is startling to realize that more than half the persons sixty-
five years of age and older have an annual income of less than
$1,000 (7). As expenses for clothing and entertainment and rent
go down, their medical and hospital expenses generally increase.
Under the much publicized Kerr-Mills Act of 1960, some recognition has been granted to those old people who are medically needy
although not necessarily eligible for old age assistance. Matching
federal funds are available to states with approved plans for medical care. Approximately twenty-five states have made some use
of Kerr-Mills funds and others are preparing plans for approval.

However, as presently set up, such medical assistance is usually
meted out by local departments of welfare. Recipients must be
virtually indigent. Eligibility is often hedged around by innumerable qualifications and penalties, and the applicant must often
feel that he is a "charity case" and a burden on society. The King-
Anderson Bill, recently defeated by the Congress, was intended to
inprove this situation (and in the long run simplify administrative
problems) by having hospitalization assistance for the aged become part of the earned benefits of social security. Social security
financing of health care for the aged is seen by many to be a far more
humane answer to the problem of unbearable medical expenses in
later life.

Other legislative acts in recent years which can directly aid
the low-income patient are changes in social security coverage and
benefits. Lately, for example, widow's benefits have been increased.
Minimum benefits have been raised. Men as well as women have
been given the option of retiring and becoming eligible for social
security at age sixty-two, and the departments of the permanently
disabled have been included as beneficiaries. At this point, almost
all categories of the employed are potentially eligible for social
security.

EMOTIONAL NEEDS

Too little attention is being devoted to the emotional problems of the aged. Two separate studies of referrals to social
service at New York Hospital, for example, revealed that in con-

trast to other age groups, people over sixty in both the outpatient and inpatient services are least likely to be referred for intensive long-term casework (8,9). They are most likely to be referred for brief services requiring contact with an outside agency, such as the department of welfare, if they are outpatients. On the inpatient service, they are most likely to be referred for arrangements for care in the community, such as nursing homes or terminal care. But they are rarely referred for emotional help. Once the patient had been referred for other reasons, caseworkers were found to be uncovering basic problems which necessitated more prolonged and deeper help.

How prevalent are referrable emotional problems? A few statistics from our Study of Nursing and Psychosocial Needs of Elderly Patients at New York Hospital seem to offer some clue (1,2). Of the 167 patients interviewed by a social worker about 40 per cent were found to have problems in the area of family relationships and morale that were rated by the interviewer as moderate or serious (as compared to slight or unremarkable).

Gradually, some of the environmental problems that traditionally brought old people to social agencies are being solved by expanded public and private services. The future bids us pay attention *now* to the subtler problems of the spirit—apathy, loneliness, boredom, feelings of being unloved and unwanted.

REASONS FOR REFERRAL

As mentioned previously, not only are there more services for the elderly, but many of the services enable the disabled to remain in their own homes. Therefore, public health nurses will increasingly have opportunities to detect in their elderly patients the kind of problems that would benefit from casework. Some situations found in the Study of Nursing and Psychosocial Needs of Elderly Patients illustrate instances in which the nurse would consider referring the patient for casework (1,2).

Situations Where Defenses Cover Deep-seated Anxieties. A frequent defense discovered was denial. "I'm never alone for a minute," insists widowed, seventy-two-year-old Mrs. Rosen, but a thoughtful examination of her daily activities shows her to be almost completely isolated.

Inappropriate withdrawal and stereotyping were other common types of adjustment to anxiety. Mrs. Kubichek is only sixty-three, has been retired one year from her job as a domestic, and recently started receiving old age assistance through the department of welfare. Her depression might be guessed from her deep sighs, but her matter-of-fact statements sound deceptively "adjusted."

She says, "An old lady like me doesn't bother much with going out..... The church socials are for the youngsters. Oh, some of my old lady friends still go, but I say the place for the old is at home..... People ask too many questions. Better to leave 'em alone. Where I get my money is my business."

Conflicts Between the Patient's Culture or Background and the Environment. Mrs. Boroff, Lithuanian-born, peppery, forthright, independent, and outspoken in her language, is a source of embarrassment to her conventional son and daughter-in-law with whom she must live since her last heart attack. In their suburb of white-collar workers and well-groomed matrons, old Mrs. Boroff's peasant bluntness is conspicuous. Feeling the subtle disapproval around her reinforces the widow's feelings of being unwanted in her old age.

Mr. Cartelli has left his home and his Italian neighbors on a busy side street in Manhattan and now lives in the orderly garden apartment of his son on the other side of town. He feels alien in his new community where "nobody speaks my language," and where, in fact, most of the residents are American-born, young parents.

When the Patient Needs More Protection or Supervision. Mrs. Lyons is a retired, unlicensed practical nurse, widowed many years, now living alone. She has not been to clinic for about eight months. Her last diagnosis included hypertensive cardiovascular disease and severely handicapping bilateral senile cataracts. She sits in her rocker in her three-room apartment, clothes strewn on every chair, dust on every table top, cracked and dirty dishes in the sink.

She thoughtfully describes her problems, "I've got a funny feeling in my heart, like the blood wants to go through and it's stopped. It feels better in bed and the doctor says it's best I stay in bed but I have to do my work. I can't stay in bed. I need pills badly but I can't go out to get them. . . . I run all night to the bathroom. No, I can't get to the clinic, but a visiting nurse could at least help me lift my legs and get in and out of the bathtub. . . . Welfare sent me a lady to clean but they don't know she hardly ever comes and one girl stolt $50 from the oatmeal jar. I don't know where all the money goes. . . . . I lay here hungry, dirty. I got pain in my heart and no medicine."

Financial Problems. Mrs. Thompson needs a hearing aid but her limited social security income barely covers her rent and food and transportation to the clinic.

Mr. Finch is a watchman who privately confides that more and more he dozes on the job, and the stairs that he must walk on his nightly round are exhausting. But if he gives up this job now, how will he and his wife maintain their apartment, their daily needs, and payments of the life insurance, and still hold on to the sum they've set aside for burial expenses. Explaining his reluctance to become dependent on the family and the city, he says, "A man can't just put his pride in his pocket."

Strained Household or Family Relationships. "What can I do? I'm an outsider in another woman's home," says Mrs. Black, describing her losing battle for status in the house of her daughter-in-law. "They say, 'Ma, you stay out of this,' or 'Ma, you shouldn't be on your feet that long.' All I'd really like is to get into that kitchen and show them a really good meal. But I have to keep the peace so I try to keep my mouth shut."

Mr. Isaacs has retired and suddenly the lifetime adjustment of his marriage seems threatened. Where work and companions on the job structured his time, his conversation, and his needs for sociability, he now finds an emptiness reflected in bickering and hostile silences at home in which, "We got nothing to say to each other."

Where "Time Hangs Heavy." Mrs. Goldberg can no longer afford trips, expensive entertaining, frequent outings with friends. Her energies have diminished. Embarrassment over her reduced income and exaggerated fears about her heart have led her to curtail even reasonable activities and to withdraw from friends.

Mr. Mark feels "like a kind of castaway person." His best companion died, his neighborhood is changing as the old familiar stores, taverns, and homes of friends are giving way to high rent apartment houses, and he plaintively asks where he can go "for a little talk, a little excitement."

A Change in Living Arrangements. Mr. James, widowed and distant from his children, wonders whether to give up his apartment with its friendly, familiar belongings and move to a hotel. Perhaps he should take a roomer for companionship and protection. His occasional dizziness, his "bad days" worry him. "What if I die alone in my sleep?"

Mrs. Williams, since the progression of her arthritis, says she is no longer able to do her spring cleaning and feels, for the first time, inadequate, enfeebled, and truly old.

Mrs. O'Leary stoically sold her furniture, packed her few belongings and, at the age eighty-one, entered the free sectarian home for the aged poor in her neighborhood. She is relieved to have supervision of her diabetic regimen. She enjoys the services that were difficult for her to accomplish herself since glaucoma diminished her ability to see. However, she shrinks from the lack of privacy in the sleeping quarters she shares with eight other women. Anxiously, she reiterated her gratitude to the home, which makes it difficult for her to express her needs and preferences.

All the foregoing problems merit the attention of a caseworker. In providing the optimum care to the elderly, social workers and nurses—and doctors as well—must constantly be aware of the complementary nature of their functions.

As the nurse helps an elderly patient to eat selectively and appropriately, or to climb the stairs more ably, to integrate his daily activities into a more healthful routine, to understand and apply his medication regimen, the old person gains comfort and health. The social worker may help him to accept the limitations of aging and illness, to find new avenues of recreation, and new roles to play in his family. She may secure a variety of aids to enable him to see and hear and function better, so the old person can make the most of his age and his health.

The functions of both professionals are to ameliorate and re-store. Both should provide empathy and appreciation that is sadly lacking in the lives of many older persons. The nurse and social worker together are more effective than either alone.

REFERENCES

1. Schwartz, Doris: Nursing needs of chronically ill ambulatory patients. *Nurs. Res., 9*:185-188, Fall 1960.
2. ———: Medication errors made by elderly patients. *Amer. J. Nurs., 62*:51-53, Aug. 1962.
3. Freidson, Eliot: *Patients' View of Medical Practice.* New York, Russell Sage Foundation, 1961.
4. Newton, Kathleen: *Geriatric Nursing.,* 3d., St. Louis, C.V. Mosby Co., 1960, pp. 60-127.
5. Keller, M.D., and Smith, Charlotte: Meals on wheels: 1960. *Geriatrics, 16*:237-247, May 1961.
6. Maxwell, Jean M.: *Centers for Older People.* New York, National Council on the Aging, 1962.
7. U.S. National Advisory Committee for the White House Conference on Aging: *Background Paper on Income Maintenance.* Washington, D.C., Government Printing Office, 1961, p. 75.
8. Henley, Barbara: Social service activity with sample patients prior to onset of the study. Research memo, part of the *Study of Nursing and Psychosocial Needs of Elderly Ambulatory Patients.* (Unpublished)
9. Ullmann, Alice: Referrals and services in a medical social work department. *Soc. Ser. Rev. 35*:258-267, Sept. 1961.

COUNSELING THE OLDER PERSON*

Kathryn Ann Beatty

AMERICAN SOCIETY HAS created a special generation of older people. By glorifying family and friends, work, and health, society has caused its citizens to overemphasize these areas in their personal lives. Consequently, these areas have become the habitual avenues of need satisfaction for our older people, and other areas, such as recreation, have never been developed. Other than forcing one into a narrow approach to life, this concentration would not be a problem if it were not for the fact that often these three avenues are closed within the same relatively short time span in the older person's life. An older individual may very likely find himself suddenly without a spouse and close friends, a job, and physical vigor. Very few older people are prepared for these losses. Some oldsters begin to recognize that these three main avenues will not always be open to them for need satisfaction, but knowing how important they are, refuse to think about how these losses will affect their lives. Others know that these losses will occur, but after spending a lifetime in developing these particular avenues, feel that there is not time to change long-established patterns. Still other older people are caught completely unprepared for these inevitable losses, or if realizing that these losses will come, are not aware, until the actual incidents, how important these three avenues have become as means for satisfying their major needs. Even those who do recognize the inevitability of these losses, and who realize what these losses will mean to them, usually do not anticipate that the three main avenues will be closed concurrently.

---

*Nursing Homes, Sept. 1962.

ALL HAVE LOSSES

All people in every age group experience personal losses. A young man is not promoted in his job as he had hoped. A middle-aged woman suffers an illness that leaves her bed-fast the rest of her life. A youngster's mother or father dies. These are all obstacles in avenues for need satisfaction. However, except in rare instances, these individuals are able to adjust to these losses. Many avenues of need satisfaction are open to them, not only because they are younger, but because they have not yet centered their need satisfactions in the avenue that was destroyed. The young man can try new approaches to reach the same goal, or he can satisfy his need for achievement in some area of his life other than his job. The young woman can also satisfy the needs she was previously satisfying through being physically active by other means. The youngster may have deep scars as a result of the sudden, unexpected death, but here, too, can learn to satisfy his needs for love and security through other channels. Why, then, does the older person seem incapable of seeking new avenues when old, established ones are no longer available? The difference is that the older person may suffer two or three major losses at the same time. Even the oldster who has the most realistic outlook on life will find this difficult to bear. Society has not made it any easier for him by its degree of emphasis on these three avenues. In fact, family, work, and health are presented as goals in themselves, and as a man grows older he invests much of his energy and time in preserving and building upon them. When he does experience losses in one of these areas, instead of seeking new areas for need satisfaction, he often places increased importance on the other two. He loses his family and friends through death, so he spends a few more hours at the office each night. He has a stroke, so he places more and more emphasis on his family and friends. Because these three areas have come to mean so much to him, when he experiences losses in them he feels that a part of himself is gone too. His self-concept has become identified so closely with these particular people and states of being that when they are gone, he sees himself as a "smaller" person.

NATION-WIDE INTEREST

The particular problems of the aging have recently received nation-wide publicity, and within the past few years, these problems have caught the attention of individuals, government agencies, and industrial concerns who deal with large groups of older people. Because society has not prepared older people for the inevitable losses of life, the need for counseling immediately prior to, at the time, and after the losses has become essential today. Counseling at this point in a man's life necessarily becomes a "repair job." As counselors, we cannot look backward in the man's life and say to him that he should have prepared for the future by developing many avenues of need satisfaction. We cannot, when we are face-to-face with the individual who has already overemphasized a few areas, say that society was wrong to worship these areas. We cannot glibly tell him that he should not have identified so strongly with such a few things or people so that he feels that parts of himself have been taken away with their loss. True as this may be, we must help the individual look ahead with a positive self-concept because, for him, his past cannot be changed.

Many older people with whom the counselor comes in contact will indicate that they feel in the way, useless, and unwanted. Even the aggressive older person who is still fighting to protect himself from further losses will show how he really feels inside. What happens, then, is that others around him soon begin to agree with him, saying, "Yes, you are no longer needed, loved, or even important to yourself. Isn't it a pity." By doing this, they reflect back to the older person their agreement, so that his original self-concept is reinforced by how others react toward him. Nothing weakens one's positive self-concept more quickly than sensing that others believe one is no longer capable of directing his own life. How, then, are we to react toward the older person who is trying to feel important and "whole" again, after he has experienced "parts" of his self being destroyed? Because human beings absorb into their self-concept what is reflected to them through the attitudes and actions of others, the counselor must react toward the older person in such a way as to help him rebuild a positive self-concept. The counselor must make the older person feel that he believes the following things about him:

1) That he is important to himself and to society. Even if the older person is totally helpless physically, he can be made to feel that he is important in making the lives of those with whom he comes in daily contact happier.

2) That he is worthy of respect. Every human being, because he was created human, is deserving of respect. This the counselor must remember, However, individuals like to be respected as individuals and not merely because they are like everyone else. The counselor must seek to find quality or qualities that each individual possesses which are worthy of respect. By respecting the older person, first as a human being, and secondly as an individual, the counselor is helping him regain his own self -respect if he has lost it.

3) That he is capable of making decisions and governing his own life, within the limits of his present means. The counselor who conveys to his client that he expects the client to try to make decisions in the counseling setting and in everyday life, will be significantly building up the client's desire and ability to do so.

4) That the counselor wants to listen to the older person in an effort to try to understand him. The older person often feels misunderstood, and it is through the airing of feelings in an atmosphere of understanding and acceptance that the older person will arrive at insights in understanding himself.

5) That the older person is encouraged to proceed at his own rate in working out his problems. Each person has "breaking points" which should not be transcended all at once. The older person who feels uncomfortable at points in the counseling interview should be allowed to "slow down" or if he seems to be proceeding further and further into highly emotional areas, the counselor should help him slow down. This is especially important to remember when counseling an individual who has recently experienced several losses.

BE CONSISTENT

These attitudes of the counselor should remain consistent throughout all contacts with the older person. These, of course, do not exhaust the nature of the attitudes conveyed to the client by the counselor, but are indicative only of the type of feelings every counselor should have toward every client during every meeting with him.

Each older person is an individual and must be treated as an individual first, and as an "older" individual only when this assists the counselor in his understanding of his client. Because of the uniqueness of each individual's background and self-concept, there will be "variables" in the counseling situation. Some of these are mentioned below merely to remind the counselor not to become rigid in his relationship with different clients or with the same client throughout the counseling process:

1. Each older person will require varying degrees of support from the counselor. If a man has suffered several personal losses he may need more support than one who has not or who has seemed to have adjusted to these losses. Older people who have "given up," who are quarrelsome, or who are complainers may all need the same amount of support, but different kinds. As an individual gains or loses strength during the interview, he will need corresponding support.

2. The physical setting of the counseling situation should be different for each client, and should be changed with the same client if a change is indicated. What may be appropriate for "most people" may not be for a specific client. Some older people will feel more comfortable in a very structured situation with the counselor behind his desk in his office. Other older people may progress more rapidy while sitting in a position where they will not have to look directly at the counselor. It may be advisable to see the older person in surroundings that are familiar to him, where he can structure the situation himself. Fear of both an unfamiliar setting and a stranger may cause the older person to get off to a slower start than is necessary. The counselor

should be ready to change the environment of the counseling interviews to meet the varying needs of his clients.

3. The counselor should be willing to adapt his tempo to that of the client's. Although the anticipated outcome of the interviews should always be in the counselor's mind, he must also be aware of the importance of the process by asking himself continually what effect he has on his client's present self-concept by the nature of his lead, his suggestions, his encouragement, or his silence. The communication of feeling between the counselor and the older person is paramount in the entire counseling process, for the feelings others communicate to us are the materials from which our self-concept is built. If the counselor reacts inappropriately by "leading" the client too much, and communicates to the client that he is really not capable of making his own decisions, the client will begin to feel inadequate once again.

SUMMING UP

To sum up these main points, it can be said that underlying attitudes must remain constant in the counselor's relationships with all older people at all times throughout the counseling process. With these attitudes for a foundation, the counselor should adapt his techniques to the individual and should be willing to change his techniques with the same individual.

Counseling older people is not much different from counseling any other age group when one tries to see them as they see themselves. It might help the counselor who is working with older people to ask himself these questions in an effort to understand this client and how this client sees himself: What losses has this client suffered? What did these losses mean to him? How will it be possible to help him accept these losses, to change his long-established way of life? What avenues of need satisfaction are available for this particular individual? How can I help this person plan for the expected and unexpected things in life? The task of the counselor who works with the aged is not easy, but it need not be hopeless so long as he believes that anyone is capable of "bouncing back" and adequately meeting and directing his own life. The older person needs, more than anything else, the counselor's faith that he can succeed.

HEALTH CARE—RESPONSIBILITY OF STATE OR SOCIETY*

S. L. Sparks

IN THE FREE NATIONS of Europe, socialized medicine is providing health care for thousands of underprivileged persons who formerly received no medical attention, but while it heals the bodies of a few, it seems to be infecting the minds of the masses.

Government subsidies, particularly in the field of medicine and old age pensions, appear to be robbing the average European of his initiative and his willingness to compete in a free enterprise system. He is inclined to place a higher value on security than on individual achievement.

The widespread—and apparently growing—fear of competition in Europe might well be illustrated by the reactions and philosophies of two West Germans and an Italian interviewed by our group of twenty-six American nursing home administrators, doctors, bankers and building contractors who specialize in the building of nursing homes, during a recent thirty-day tour of Europe.

We made the tour to study the philosophy and methods of patient care under government regulations, the degree of control exercised by the various governments, and the effects of socialized medicine and health care.

Joe Michaels, a personable and obviously intelligent college graduate in his early 30's, served as our chauffeur in Frankfurt, Germany. He is married and is the father of five children. He speaks English as fluently as his own native tongue, is quick-

*Nursing Homes, Dec. 1963.

witted, resourceful, and apparently capable of assuming responsibilities.

He earns the equivalent of $200 a month, plus tips, and approximately 30 per cent of his salary is taken in direct taxes.

Impressed by Joe's apparent capabilities, a successful building contractor in our group offered him a job in America at a salary much greater than his present earnings.

Joe considered the offer, then rejected it, explaining:

"I have contributed toward my government retirement fund for eleven years. We have no medical bills to pay. West Germany recently adopted a law which will give me a substantial increase in retirement pay. My medical bills will be guaranteed and my housing needs will be met. I do not want to take the chance of losing this."

W. K. N. Skope of West Berlin is a tour conductor for the Automobile Association of America. He is an honor graduate of the University of Vienna and has studied in France. He speaks and writes five languages fluently and possesses outstanding organization abilities.

Skope met us in Copenhagen as we left the Scandinavian Airlines System plane which we had boarded in New York. He accompanied us on our tour of Denmark, Switzerland, West Germany, Italy, France, England and Scotland, acting as our guide and tour conductor, and frequently, as our interpreter.

He may be offered a promotion and transfer to New York, and if the offer is made, he probably will accept it, but not without misgivings.

He favors the socialized medicine and housing programs and the retirement pensions of West Germany and would be reluctant to abandon this wide umbrella of protection to assume financial responsibility for medical care—especially for his children—and for housing and his old age security.

"In Germany," he said, "the child receives excellent medical care at no cost from the time it is conceived until it dies of old age.

"The expectant mother receives free pre-natal care from conception to childbirth; she is accompanied from the hospital to her home by a nurse and is followed by a social worker. They jointly supervise the care and feeding of the infant. Even maid service is furnished free if needed.

"In fact," he said "West German law allows the child to be taken from its parents if the social worker decides it is not receiving proper care in their custody."

CONFIDENCE LACKING

Governmental assistance for health care is embraced as warmly in Italy as in West Germany, but the Italian businessman has less confidence in his government.

Gean Simone, Milan office manager for Scandinavian Airlines System, summarized the attitude of the Italian businessman this way:

"We like the government's medical care program but we feel the cost in taxes is too high for the benefits we receive. Too, we have no assurance that the tax we pay today for medical care will be used for that purpose tomorrow. A new government might discard the medical program in its entirety. In that case, we would lose everything we have contributed toward the program."

The feeling of insecurity experienced by the average German might stem from the fact that the nation has suffered two major military defeats within half a century.

The Italian's distrust of his government could date back to the infamous Roman Empire which rewarded the taxpayer with "bread and circuses." We made no attempt to diagnose problems of government, general economy or political philosophy, except as they related to the medical care programs.

But a superficial study seems to indicate that free Europe is geographically, politically, culturally, industrially, and philosophically divided into three general areas—the countries north of the Alps, those south of the Alps, and Great Britain.

NO SLUMS SEEN

Although the three nations are highly industrialized, the visitor sees no slum areas in the cities of Denmark, Switzerland and West Germany. Flower gardens are prevalent in both the urban and rural areas. The farms appear to be fertile, productive and well-tended.

The crisp climate north of the mountain range which arcs upward from the French-Italian border seems to spawn an energetic and ambitious breed of Homo sapiens with a sophisticated and realistic outlook on government, human relations, and domestic responsibilities—and an inherent self-sufficiency.

Socialized medicine first was introduced in Denmark early in the 19th century. Old Folks Town, a medical care center we visited in Copenhagen, was built in 1919. It employs approximately 1,000 persons to care for an average load of 1,800 patients or inmates. Its patients receive the equivalent of $9.50 a month for incidental expenses, exclusive of the hospital rooms, medical care, food and clothing.

HOME IN ZURICH

Cantonal Home Kaeferberg which we visited in Zurich, Switzerland, opened its first branch last Spring. When completed, it will include four branches spotted geographically in Zurich's major population areas and each of the four branches will accommodate 1,000 inmates. Medical care for the chronically ill patients will be provided in each of the four branches.

At present, however, the home has only 100 beds and is adding 254. Each inmate has a telephone, radio and small food storage facilities, and each has his own-closet area where his medicine is kept.

Each floor of the home includes a television room. A library, hair-dressing room and an examining room are included on the first floor.

The daily per-patient cost is the equivalent of $7.29. The patient pays $1.61 and the state pays the remainder. Persons who earn less than the equivalent of $2,500 a year generally are sent to a county home for health care.

The extravagant waste of funds for the care of the aged and the chronically ill north of the Alps is even more evident at the Nethesta Home for the Chronically Ill in Zurich. The home cost two million dollars and presently cares for 100 patients, although the number will be increased to 180. The average age of the inmates is seventy years.

The home is supported by the Lutheran Church which operates two hospitals in Zurich. It is operating with an average deficit of 10,000 francs, or $2,300. The church picks up the tab.

The tax deducted annually from the worker's pay check in Switzerland equals his salary for two months and the tax rate is increasing. However, the tax obligation is accepted as a matter of course and without complaint.

In Germany, the cost of the health care program is evaluated more carefully, but nursing home accommodations are adequate. The German businessman doesn't complain about the cost of the public health program, but he is frugal and judiciously watches for any evidence of waste. If tax inequities exist, they are not flagrant.

GERMAN ATTITUDE

The average German worker seems to realize his responsibilities to society include health care for the aged, the underprivileged and the unemployables, and he seems willing to shoulder the burden. He is too busy to worry about the details.

Foremost among the German nursing homes is the Home for the Aged in Frankfurt. Built by the Johanna Kirchner Foundation and sponsored by the Workers Welfare Association, the home was founded shortly after World War I, then closed when Hitler came into power. It was re-opened in 1945.

Here the cost of nursing care per patient is three dollars a day and if the patient's government pension is inadequate, the debit is absorbed by government subsidies.

The cost for the care of ambulatory patients varies from $1.88 to $2.38 a day, contingent upon the type of room and the individual need for attention by a doctor. Here again, the government picks up the tab if the patient is unable to pay.

A sharp contrast can be noted in Italy where the average businessman doesn't bother to disguise his distrust of the government. The sentiments of Gean Simone were reiterated by Father Opera D. Guanella, director of the Institute Don Guanella for Aged Men in Rome.

"The taxation is not honest." he said. "The rich people will do anything to cut their taxes and most of them pay less than their share."

The padre has his problems with the governmental bureaucracies. The Italian government computes the cost of patient care in state-supported homes at the equivalent of $1.28 a day. However, when the same patient is transferred to Institute Don Guanella, the government cuts its contribution to 80 cents a day, and the resulting deficit must be absorbed by private contributions.

Socialized medicine is not yet recognized by name in Italy, but one of four owners of a posh privately-owned Milan institution which caters to the wealthy patient said:

"We know Italy will have socialized medicine. All we can do is delay it."

ENGLISH PROBLEMS

In England, the taxpayer generally favors socialized medicine and the program seems to be working successfully.

But England is not without her problems. These include inequities in payments to doctors for their services, a shortage of general practitioners, a need for more nursing home and hospital facilities, and a lack of public funds necessary to build and equip new facilities needed to provide care for all those who need and are entitled to it.

Although thousands of persons who were totally without medical care before socialized medicine was introduced now receive some medical care, it is all too often inadequate.

To offset the need for additional facilities which cannot be supplied, England is instituting an educational program to encourage the treatment of patients in their own homes. The program is being successfully used in Denmark and is expected to ease the load on Britain's nursing homes and hospitals.

This new concept of patient care offers two immediate advantages. It relieves overcrowded condition in health care institutions and it allows the patient to remain in familiar surroundings with his family and friends.

The inequities in the medical profession in England under the socialized medicine program arise from the fact that the government does not pay the general practitioner adequately for his services. He must administer to 2000-2400 patients a year to earn as much as $8,500 a year. He complains that he is unable to devote enough time to individual patients, thus depriving them of proper health care due them under the government program.

Meantime, the doctors who have earned Merit Awards and serve as consultants and surgeons in the hospitals can easily earn as much as $22,500 a year.

Despite this problem, however, England's medical schools have long waiting lists of young men and women eager to enter the medical profession. They believe, as most Englishmen do, that the problem of income inequities will be resolved in the near future.

NO PRIVATE HOMES

One striking similarity was found in all the European countries we visited. We were unable to find any privately-owned nursing homes in Europe and social workers assured us there is no opportunity for private enterprise in this field.

Europe is doing an outstanding job in physical rehabilitation and occupational therapy in its nursing homes—a field in which American nursing homes are sadly deficient. The reason is obvious. European governments realize the need of therapy and shoulder the cost. In the United States, the state welfare authorities determine the subsidized cost of medical and health care for nursing home patients and some states will not underwrite the costs of physical rehabilitation and occupational therapy.

This brings up the delicate question of the extent of the state's responsibility for health care in America.

The national debate now raging in this country as to whether the welfare state or private enterprise will predominate in health care is far from inconsequential. Beneath the surface of this controversy is a desperate bid for political power, and it is not a question of Communism versus Americanism. No doubt the advocates of both programs are equally certain their plans are conductive to the greatest common good.

The controversy might be resolved more readily if the advocates of both plans would concede the desirability of the ends pursued while focusing attention on new methods of achieving them. The welfare state need not be the sole dispenser of welfare. It might be found that the state could establish a legal framework within which private enterprise could operate—a framework which recognizes individual welfare as a social responsibility without necessarily being a direct responsibility of the state.

President Kennedy believes his Medicare Bill offers the best solution of the problem created by increased medical costs coupled with a longer life span. But it might not be, and the truth can be determined only after years of experimentation.

Meantime, the state is subsidizing health and medical care in certain areas, and the federal Social Security program is accepted and apparently successful.

But it is significant that we also have a program of non-governmental health and medical insurance in America, and that an estimated two-thirds of the nation's population are now covered by health and medical care insurance issued by such non-profit organizations as Blue Cross and Blue Shield, or by private insurance companies.

Would it not be prudent to encourage this natural trend, matching any state program with a private program, thus giving the individuals the option of choosing between state and private enterprise programs? Compulsory medical insurance is one thing while it is quite another to make only one kind of medical insurance compulsory.

The relative cost of the two programs might prove that private enterprise could offer a more economical method of solving the problem of medical care for the aged and underprivileged. The taxpayer is going to pay the bill, regardless of the method. The idea that somehow people will get more from the government than they put in is appealing but baseless. Government money is not something apart from the people's money—it IS the people's money.

The illusion that government can be financed by the rich is equally appealing, but equally baseless. The cost of the government is infinitely greater than the ability of the rich to pay for it. The major portion of the cost must be borne by that vast majority of taxpayers who think they are poorer than they really are. This group must subsidize medical care for the really poor under any program instituted.

We are now in the process of deciding how much we wish to spend on medical care, as compared to such things as education, leisure and luxuries. It seems likely that we will decide to spend more for medicine, but it does not necessarily follow that the federal government is the only agency competent to administer the health program.

I believe the American businessman is the smartest and most capable man ever produced by any civilization, and I believe he can—and will—solve the problem of health care by private enterprise, IF he ever slows down long enough to do it.

But I believe time is running out. Just as water flows to seek its own level, government flows into a vacuum.

I expressed this opinion in a private conversation with P. H. Constable, chairman of the Hospital Centre in London.

He said flatly:

"Mr. Sparks, time has run out. America will have socialized medicine!"

August 19, 1963—Copenhagen, Denmark

. . . There are some private rooms, 2- 3- and 4-bed rooms, and a few wards. These people may bring their own furniture, except for beds. Some had beautiful antique furniture, such as chests, clocks, pictures, and chairs.

. . . They eat only one hot meal a day at noon and are served a continental breakfast of coffee, tea, milk or chocolate, danish pastry, butter and jam. These people are used to this, as Europeans normally eat such a breakfast, a main meal being at noon, and a light supper in the evening. Staff members bring their own lunch, and are not allowed to eat here.

Det Mosaiske Troessamfund Nursing Home

We visited the Jewish Nursing Home, which is also run by the Government. This home is only two years old, very modern and lovely, with beautiful grounds and the latest equipment. They are building a larger one, as this one only has thirty-two beds and there is a waiting list of forty.

. . . The building is a two-story structure and cost $1,6000,000; however, there is so much wasted space they could easily accommodate twice as many patients as they presently have.

The R.N's train three years and one additional year for their degrees. They work seven and one-half hours a day, six days a week.

August 22—Johanna Kirchner Stifung Nursing Home, Frankfurt, Germany

The Executive Secretary of Nurses accompanied us on our tour of this Home. The home is divided into two buildings, one for ambulatory patients, and the other for nursing care. There are 100 in each building. This home is sponsored by the Workers Welfare Association.

... The dining and reception rooms join, and have a glass partition between them. They open on a lovely flower garden, with a small lake behind it. In the reception room, they have a T. V., a library, and a huge aquarium tank. Each room opens on a small balcony, and each balcony has a flower box. In the dining room, there is a stage, and about fifty plays are presented there each year.

August 24—Altersheim am Bruderholz Nursing Home— Basel, Switzerland

This home is operated and owned by the Municipal Welfare. ...It is very much like the others we had seen, in that it is new, luxurious, and has much wasted space. We first went to the kitchen, which is all stainless steel. They have seventy-two patients and average about 10 per cent ill temporarily. They do not keep bed patients, however, as these are sent to either hospitals or "Chronic Homes."

For these seventy-two patients, they have only one cook and one helper, one R.N., and nine aides and cleaners.

SENIOR CITIZEN AT THE CROSSROADS*

W HAT CHANCE DOES A sixty-five-year-old man or woman have to live out an expected fifteen or more years of life with dignity and some sense of satisfaction?

According to expressed desires of average aging individuals, they want more than anything else to live their retirement years independently at home—be it in a house, hotel, or an apartment.[2] They hope, too, that they will receive adequate medical care in a hospital nearby in times of severe disability and their terminal illness. How often do their lives turn out this way?

All too many times a senior citizen finds that on retirement he is suddenly thrust into a strange world, and there is little or no place for him in it. His income is fixed, and with it he tries to meet constant increases in his rent or taxes, and in his bills for fuel, other utilities, and insurance. He may try to manage his affairs by denying himself social contacts or adequate nutrition. But as all of his expenses continue to edge upward, he loses control over them; eventually, it takes no more than a fall, a fracture, a failing heart, or just increased feebleness to reduce his fragile plans to a shamble.

Then he finds himself surrounded by anxious relatives, concerned neighbors, or more-or-less interested representatives from community agencies. And he either hears or senses the question which is paramount in the minds of all of them: "Now what are we going to do with grandpa?"—or old Mr. Baker, old Mrs. Jones —or whoever the senior citizen may be to his own family or to his community.

*Whats' New, 214:10-15, 1959, Courtesy of Abbott Laboratories.

What to do, indeed; the echo of this question is heard in every community in the world. The loud controversy over costs of the services of physician, nurse and hospital has obscured another problem as vital to life and well-being of the senior citizen—his problem of securing and maintaining suitable living arrangements which meet his changing needs and resources in his later years.

A senior citizen is fortunate when he lives in a community where there are foresighted individuals who realize that his problem with aging is an inseparable triad of interacting problems with his housing, health and money. In such communities he has a better opportunity to deal effectively with his housing problem; and then he can remain longer with his cherished possessions, the familiar faces and scenes, where he will be able to retain the prized privilege of making some independent decisions; and be more able to live on his own resources.

Rochester, New York, is one of these communities.[3] In 1957, a group of public-spirited men in Rochester formed a nonprofit organization to provide some housing for the long neglected aged in their community whose incomes were too low to secure any housing in the open market, and too high for them to be eligible for any public housing. In 1958, they completed Cobbs Hill, a seventy-apartment building where a senior citizen over sixty-five years, with a weekly income of under $65, can rent an apartment for an average monthly cost of $17 per room.

These rentals are without cost to taxpayers. The state approved use of park land donated by the city of Rochester; the sponsors raised 10 per cent of the building costs; and the state took a mortgage for the remainder under New York's Limited Profit Housing Program (Mitchell-Lama Act, 1955). This act was passed to encourage private capital to finance housing for middle-income residents of this state. To keep rentals within their reach the return on invested funds is limited to six percent, and these self-liquidating mortgages bear a low interest rate and long amortization periods which coincide with the rate of interest and term of state bonds issued to cover the loans.

Rochester citizens were so gratified with Cobbs Hill that they have a second seventy-five-apartment building under construction for their senior citizens. It is not surprising that the number of eligible applicants exceeds the apartments that will be available—for the senior citizen who now lives in Cobbs Hill retains his dignity—he is paying his own way. And he has a more reasonable proportion of his fixed income left for other necessities, such as adequate nutrition, care of his health, and health insurance. But what is more satisfying to him is his relief from his anxiety over the increase in taxes or rent which would force him out of his home into a less desirable neighborhood among strangers.

For a senior citizen who lives at Cobbs Hill, satisfactory housing turns out to be a close ally of effective preventive medicine.

Oklahoma City. Chances for a satisfying life are improving for the 30,000 or more men and women in Oklahoma City who are over sixty-five. Under the leadership of their physicians, the recently organized "Senior Citizens, Incorporated,"[4] completed a three-year study and investigation of some 200 facilities and programs for senior citizens. The nonprofit organization, composed of sixty leaders for church and civic organizations in the city, now has a published plan for a new kind of well balanced community for senior citizens. It will occupy 320 acres at the edge of Oklahoma City; they plan residences for 500 aging individuals in the next five years.

The plan calls for a center which supplements but does not duplicate any facilities or services for older people in Oklahoma City. A convalescent and rehabilitation hospital in the new community will care for residents in an emergency or a minor illness, but its main function will be to care for senior citizens during convalescence or rehabilitation when they return from general hospitals in the city. All patients will remain under the care of their own private physicians. Ambulant patients in the community or surrounding area in need of rehabilitation will be treated at the center; both occupational and recreational therapy will be provided.

The cafeteria in connection with the hospital will serve meals to ambulant patients, staff, residents who desire an occasional meal away from home, or to their guests. There will be a small shopping center for basic needs; an auditorium for concerts, lectures or social events; sheltered workshops; and an interdenominational chapel where the senior citizen may attend a service in his own faith when he is unable to reach his church in Oklahoma City.

Encircling the circumference of the center will be the cottages, apartments, or rooms in larger buildings for residents. All of the homes will have the safety features needed to prevent accidents and injuries to the aged; and all of the streets are planned to prevent through traffic. A buzzer system will connect the home of each resident with the center so that no aged individual in this new community need fear sudden injury or illness without aid. When it is advisable, a nurse will care for the senior citizen in his home.

Church groups and civic organizations interested in providing retirement homes for their members will build most of the homes, and control admissions to their own residences. Money for the center will be raised mostly by these interested groups and individuals. By grouping their homes about the center, all of its facilities and services will be available to the members in each residence. The cost of such a center would be prohibitive to each group, if it built in an isolated location.

Physicians in Oklahoma City will gain an invaluable new community resource to aid them in the care of their aging patients; and senior citizens in the new community will have an opportunity to live more years independently, because of better housing, maintenance of health, and for rehabilitation in case of disability.

Santa Barbara, California. A six-year-old senior center in Santa Barbara[5] was built for older residents of that county who could not obtain suitable housing with low incomes. Foundations, organizations and individuals donated $200,000, which covered the cost of the land, twenty-nine row cottages and the clubhouse, in the hope that this center would encourage other communities to provide more comfortable and independent living for their senior citizens.

These modest homes, built around small, sunny patios, are pleasantly surrounded with trees, grass and flowers. They rent for $35 a month, utilities included. The thirty men and women who live there are between sixty-seven and eighty-four years old. Each has a living room with a recessed kitchen unit, and a bedroom with bath. They take pride in their homes, and special pleasure in having their own kitchens and bathrooms.

All have the use of the clubhouse where there is a colorful lounge with fireplace, an enclosed patio, a community kitchen and laundry. A hostess in charge of the center lives in the clubhouse, and other groups in Santa Barbara use it for recreational and educational activities. This brings the community life to the doorstep of the senior citizens who live there, and makes life there both pleasant and interesting.

The senior center is operated by the Santa Barbara Unit of the American Women's Voluntary Services; it is self-sustaining, and the waiting list of eligible applicants for these homes makes it necessary to select a new resident on the basis of greatest need.

A healthy, active senior citizen who has most of his lifetime savings in his mortgage-free home,[6] where he expects to live free from rent worries, may be forced out of it and into an overcrowded house with his children, when his tax bill gets so high that it takes an unreasonable portion of his fixed income. Then a hole in the roof of his house, or a breakdown in his heating plant, may be a disaster because the cost of repair is beyond his means. Generally speaking, FHA loans are not available to an elderly person.

He or his family may decide that the time has come for him to sell his home and seek more economical living arrangements. When this painful transaction is completed, both he and his children may be shocked to find that a 25 per cent federal capital gains tax, a six-per cent realtor's fee, legal and other closing costs will leave him with few "48-cent" dollars to secure suitable living arrangements for the expected period of his remaining years. They decide that he should conserve what he has left for future hospital and medical costs; he moves in with his children against his own wishes and those of his children.

In Santa Barbara, a group of individuals headed by Mr. and Mrs. Adrian G. Wood became concerned about this forced three-generation living and the burdens it placed on families. Wood Glen Hall, Inc., was formed, a nonprofit, charitable corporation.[7] Mr. and Mrs. Wood donated to the corporation land and funds which were used in the construction of Wood Glen Hall for the benefit of the senior citizen whose circumstances would force him to live with his children. The home was built around the best plan and design that could be obtained for a building to house elderly residents, and it has a comfortable, homelike atmosphere. The building completely encircles two patios designed for outdoor living and recreation; it occupies four acres in a fine residential district, near shopping and transportation facilities.

The nonprofit organization operates Wood Glen Hall so that senior citizens may live there at a minimum cost, which covers maintenance and administration, and their food. At present this cost is $155 a month for a resident, and this is the only charge made. Wood Glen has accommodations for fifty-one residents who must be in good health, ambulant, mentally active, willing and able to adjust to group living. No nursing or medical care is provided, and residents must be hospitalized or go elsewhere for care when ill or disabled.

Three well-chosen meals are served in the dining room each day, and there are small kitchens for snacks or entertaining. Barbecues are on the patio. The elderly resident has the use of two living rooms with fireplaces and TV; and a larger one with a stage and screen for movies. There is a room for arts and crafts work, and another for meditations.

Each room has its own temperature control and two-way intercommunication system which connects it with administration offices. A staff of seventeen maintains the home, but the residents are expected to keep their own rooms in order. This beautiful home is kept in excellent condition throughout.

Only residents of California are eligible to live at Wood Glen; preference is given those from surrounding counties, and especially those with no home except in the house of their children.

The average age of the thirty women residents is 80.3 years; that of the ten men, 78.6 years. They may come and go, entertain their families and friends, or even work outside the premises.

The design, plan and features of this residence offer many valuable suggestions to those planning housing for senior citizens, even though the entire cost of this over-a-million-dollar home would be prohibitive for many other communities.

In La Jolla, California,[8] some 200 women in a group at St. James Church became aware of an increasing number of lonely retired teachers, business women, or widows who were living in dreary rooms after they had spent comfortable, worthwhile years living in La Jolla. These women were not on old-age assistance or pensions, and they did not want charity. They did want independent living, but they needed companionship and the protection given by group living; and they did not have enough money to enter the homes for senior citizens in a community which charges a charter or life-lease fee. So they were trying to live alone on about $2000 a year.

The women in St. James Church decided to organize the non-profit Social Service League of La Jolla for community service and to provide a home for senior citizens. They wanted to build a self-supporting residence of small apartments, each complete with kitchenette and bathroom, and a central living-dining lounge where the main meal could be served every day. An administration office, residence for a manager, and kitchen were to be adjacent.

And this is what League House is, and much more— it provides a most satisfying way of life to the women who live there. But there were seven years of fund raising, overcoming legal problems, securing land, plan revisions and construction before it was ready for occupancy in 1955; and there was an investment of $114,353, with a $50,000 mortgage. This was paid off in three years.

Apartments at League House are real homes, furnished with valued possessions of the twenty-one women who live in them. The attractive living-dining lounge has the atmosphere of a spacious, comfortable living room in a substantial home. The administrative experience and personality of the manager contribute to this feeling of being in a private home where your hostess thoughtfully provides for your comfort, and puts you at ease.

At League House the excellent food is prepared with care, and served at a table which is candle-lighted and graced with flowers. The women in League House thoroughly enjoy the independent living they have. Though they may be over sixty when admitted, seven are past eighty, and none are under sixty-five. They aid each other and prefer to entertain themselves because they have years of associations within the community.

Physicians, hospitals, churches, the Visiting Nurse Association and other interested individuals in La Jolla refer applicants to League House. Before admission they must have a physical examination, and the League admissions committee takes into consideration their compatibility with other residents, their background and personal income.

Those in single apartments pay $90 a month; those in double apartments with separate bedroom, from $125 to $135 each. This covers general cleaning, utilities (except their private telephones), the main meal each day, but no medical care. Each apartment is connected with the manager by a buzzer system; when the manager is away she is relieved by a League volunteer or a paid substitute; someone is always on call.

When a resident is ill, the main meal is carried to her apartment; she may secure nursing care at her expense and remain in her apartment for a certain period; in the event that the physician decides she will not be ambulant again, she is aided in securing nursing-home or other care elsewhere. The women at League House make every attempt to maintain themselves in good health in order that they may remain there.

There is a long waiting list, and an addition is planned in the hope that a total of fifty residents may be given the opportunity of living at League House. The League has the satisfaction of seeing senior citizens return to their normal way of life, at a price they can afford to pay; and they have shown what citizens in a community can do for senior citizens and their problems with the private resources of the community.

The cooperative residence for retired persons is very popular with senior citizens who can afford it. Church groups with many years of experience in housing the aged are changing over from the home for the ailing aged to conform with the wish of more older people for sheltered living while still active. They build infirmaries, or arrange for nursing or hospital care for their residents in the community.

Near San Diego, California, 170 of the 220 residents in the

Methodist Homes live in cottages, and the others are in the nursing-home section. Cost of residency is based in life expectancy, which makes it higher for women than for men. At age sixty-five, life-lease ranges from $4160 to $16,500, depending upon the type of housing. While the resident lives in a cottage and does not require special services, he pays $100 a month in addition to his life lease; when unable to care for himself, another $75 a month is added. This includes medical costs, except for those ailments acquired before admission. This exclusion and others for dental care, eyeglasses or hearing aids and various other items is generally found in these life-lease contracts. A lump sum for life care on the same actuarial basis is available.

Throughout the country there are many life-lease residences for senior citizens at various levels of cost, all the way up to the luxurious, coveted resort hotels such as the White Sands, of the Southern California Presbyterian Homes, where 177 men and women pay from $7500 to $50,000 for a life lease, and $185 monthly in addition for services. Usually residents in this type of home have the privilege of leaving if they desire, and they are refunded their money minus the prorated charge for their time of residence. Generally their contract calls for a raise in the monthly payment if the cost of operating the retirement home go up. These nonprofit organizations of religious groups have tax exemptions which allow them to offer comparable accommodations at a lower cost than other private operations can; they put their surplus profits into more homes, and this cooperative type of living for the senior citizen is already big business. As a rule the church-sponsored retirement residence does not limit their admissions to members in that church.

Why do the aging with higher income levels seek these homes? The couples seek to establish a retirement home and companionship with others, so that the death of one will not make it necessary for the surviving one to make another adjustment in housing and living arrangements when left alone. At all levels of income they seek security, privacy and companionship. As they age, they dread being alone.

School teachers have made housing history with remarkable achievements in providing the life-lease residence which is within the means of the retired school teacher. When the Omaha, Nebraska, Education Association[9] applied for an FHA loan to construct a building with one-room and kitchenette apartments for their retired teachers who could not secure suitable housing, because their fixed incomes were as low as $70 to $90 a month, they were turned down because of the low incomes. With community support they were able to get an amendment to the FHA law. They secured their loan, raised the money, and have built a twelve-story building in Omaha which has 132 one-room apartments, and the other facilities usually found in these residences. The retired teachers, and some other professional retired persons, pay $1500 for their life leases, and an estimated $70 monthly for their share in the actual operating costs of the building. For those who can't pay the $1500, there is a provision to subsidize them, and no one in the residence is aware of the identity of these few deserving people. Since the teachers in Omaha got their loan and the change in FHA law in 1957, a dozen or more such homes are being planned for teachers.

Four school teachers in Iowa made a housing achievement in that state when they built the first cooperative residence for their own occupancy. A special ruling was required to give each of the four teachers a homestead tax exemption on her apartment. After a couple of years of living in their homes, these teachers say, "We're sorry we didn't do this sooner; a much less pleasant apartment cost only eight dollars a month less to rent; and by the time we retire, our retirement homes will be paid for."

These four teachers have their homes in what appears to be a large ranch-type home in a good residential part of Cedar Rapids. The attractive building was designed by a prominent architect who was interested in the novel project planned by the teachers. Each apartment is entirely separate, and has its own heating plant. The garages are concealed in wings built around an open court. The grounds and basement are community property, as is the laundry equipment. The teachers find that it is an advantage to share snow shoveling costs and other other outside maintenance expense, and it will make their fixed retirement incomes go farther.

Since they have lived there, they have found other values they appreciate greatly; there has been one fractured hip and several illnesses among them. But they get along much better when they have each other to carry in a meal, or give assistance in many other ways. This means a great deal as they approach retirement.

Their financing was unique. Two paid for their apartments; two who had little money are paying off the loan secured from a local mortgage company. The four signed the loan and an agreement to give the others the right to buy, if one must sell. Perhaps the teachers have found a way for many to share their retirement-residence cost by reducing the tax, and dividing maintenance costs by four. These four women think it's ideal, as a retirement plan.[10]

At **Grey Gables, Ojai, California,**[11] a national retirement residence for teachers has achieved a community way of life with the life-lease plan that has so many rewarding values for the eighty men and women living there that it would be difficult to imagine that there could be a more satisfactory living arrangement for them.

Flourishing trees, flowers and lawns surround apartment cottages, each apartment with its garden and porch with a place for a comfortable chair. A gardener cares for the grounds, but a third of the teachers are real dirt gardeners. Everywhere there is a view of pleasant landscape or the mountains. Inside the homes, and in the central dining room, living room, library or offices, the fresh flowers, kept there by residents, and books give Grey Gables the unobtrusive, restful beauty and friendly atmosphere of a neighborhood in a small university town. There is an impression of a life of ease.

But the telephone switchboard tells a different story of the life here—the ease is "alternated with labor." Citizens of Ojai appeal to the senior citizens in Grey Gables for help on every kind of civic project. The teachers are found on the hospital board, in city council meetings, presiding over a precinct election board or helping on the community fund drive, and in countless other places where there is work for public spirited citizens to do. Some tutor or teach part time; others make valuable contributions to the cultural life of the community.

And each day at Grey Gables they voluntarily perform the

small services which need to be done about every home to keep it a pleasant place for living. The teachers take a justifiable pride in their home.

They come here between the ages of sixty and eighty. To be admitted they must be in good physical condition, and able to get about without assistance; and the medical care program of Grey Gables is designed to keep them so. The most outstanding feature of Grey Gables is their excellent health record.

Medical care is directed by Dr. Lincoln A. Service, a practicing physician in Ojai. The ideal of his program is to give informal home care to each resident. The privacy of each patient is preserved in the doctor-patient relationship, without visual evidence of potential illnesses among the residents. The three nurses who give home care do not wear uniforms. In addition to medical care and medicines, consultants are available, and are provided when needed. There are some exclusions, such as disability acquired before admission, but each contract is individual and everything is done to make the humane and fair approach in exceptional cases. There is the individual approach to everything at Grey Gables.

Residents are free to seek the services of any physician outside the residence physician at any time, at their own expense, and, if they prefer, in other hospitals outside the community.

The medical care program provides the residents with high quality food selected to contain high protein and mineral content. It is carefully prepared and well served. Dining is a pleasant occasion here.

Each resident may pay from $4500 to $15,000 for a life lease depending on the size of his residence. At present the monthly cost of food, maintenance and medical care is $165. Earlier it was $150. A charge is never raised once it is set for a resident at time of admittance.

The generous hospitality of Grey Gables is indicated by the high chair that sits in one corner of the dining room waiting for the visiting grandchild. Residents are free to entertain; a charge is not made, but because this is a sharing community, each makes a contribution for his own guests.

Spouses of teachers have survivorship rights in their leases, and this arrangement is made for two relatives or life-long companions. In these cases the two pay an addition of 25 per cent of the cost of a life lease.

Grey Gables continues to grow. An infirmary is underway where they hope to receive disabled retired teachers for rehabilitation; and plans are made for a long-term loan for more residences that could be offered at lower rates, because the retirement incomes of many teachers will not allow them to come to Grey Gables.[11]

It has been said that Grey Gables has the best of everything, and it certainly would seem to be true. They have an ideal climate and housing and a humane approach to the problems of the aging individual. But the importance of Grey Gables lies in what it *is*—a residence owned and managed by retired teachers who seek to make their retirement years rich and meaningful. They make it a gratifying place to live, and a delightful place for their guests to visit.

Prior to 1956, only aged couples were eligible for public housing; since the law was changed to admit single aged individuals, most cities reserve more space for their needy aged, but of necessity this must be kept to a small percentage, and again countless numbers wait on these lists as they do on the lists of private housing. The Los Angeles Housing Authority increased its number of aged in public housing to 500 in 1958, and expect to have 600 elderly people in 1959.[12]

The senior citizen finds his tax-ridden, fixed income can force him out of his home, and the only living arrangement he can afford is some form of community housing. His budget is out of balance; higher and higher taxes take more than a reasonable proportion for housing costs, or force rentals beyond his reach.

Wherever there is a housing arrangement which promises to be within his means and suited to the status of his health, he seeks admission; a fortunate few find a life with dignity and some sense of satisfaction; but countless numbers join ever lengthening waiting lists.

Perhaps the senior citizen might be better off if antagonists in the controversy over his medical and hospital costs were to consider a sensible tax program for the aged which would allow them to stay at home where they prefer to be, in most cases—and where everyone else wishes they were—and leave them enough after taxes to buy nutritious food and more adequate health insurance. How much of a reduction in taxes would that take? Not a fraction of the amount of money it takes for care and rehabilitation after unsuitable housing, poor food and anxiety have contributed to a disabling injury or an illness.

REFERENCES

1. KUPLAN, L.: *Geriatrics, 13:*808-814, December 1958.
2. VAN ZONNEVELD, R. J.: *Geriatrics, 13:*668-672, October 1958.
3. McMURRAY, J. P.: Report of Commissioner of Housing, State of New York, January 1955, December 1958.
4. DE VOSE, J. W.: *Oklahoma State Medical Association, 52:*261-265, April 1958.
5. Personal communication: Senior Center of Santa Barbara, 803 Laguna Street, Santa Barbara, Cal.
6. *Social Security Bulletin,* January 1959.
7. Personal communication: Mr. and Mrs. Cecil Cooprider, Manager and Assistant Manager, Wood Glen Hall, Santa Barbara, Cal.
8. Personal communication: Mrs. H. L. Pence, Chairman, Admissions Committee, League House; Mrs. Winthrop Davis, Manager, La Jolla, Cal.
9. Sunday *World Herald,* Omaha, Nebraska, December 7, 1958.
10. LEITER, F. E., DINSDALE, L., MILLER, B., BRANDT, A.: Personal communication, *Cedar Rapids Gazette,* June 10, 1956.
11. Personal communication: E. P. Andrus, President, National Retired Teachers Association; L. A. Service, M.D., practicing physician, Ojai, and Grey Gables, Cal.
12. ROSIEN, B.: The Housing Authority of the City of Los Angeles, personal communication.

FACILITIES FOR GOOD MEDICAL CARE IN MODERN NURSING HOMES*

Richard P. Shapera, M.D., and Marvin L. Silverblatt, M.D.

Nursing homes are no longer glorified boarding houses. They are no longer places where disease is met with inactivity, pessimism and a grim wait for a fatal outcome. "Discharge" is no longer a dirty word or a rare occasion for modern nursing homes.

Today's nursing homes are facilities for medical *care,* with emphasis on the word "care." In most cases they are stepping stones to a patient's return to his home and family. A positive program is charted for each medical problem and optimistically pursued. With the possible exception of carcinoma, patients come to nursing homes to get better, not to die. Any hospital administrator can tell you that there are many, far too many, long-term stays in general hospitals. These are totally unnecessary. The existence of excellent nursing homes provide for the care of every one of these cases. Let's look at these long-term patients. Who are they? They represent cases of cerebrovascular accidents, paraplegia, amputation, post-fracture problems including body casts or traction, post-operative neurosurgical conditions, and malignant lesions (some treated by radiation therapy).

LONG STAYS HURT

Let it be emphasized that the current status of long hospital stays is beneficial to no one. Hospitals can ill afford to have a bed "tied up" for such long periods of time, usually months. The patient can ill afford general hospital costs for this period of time and, as a rule, hospitalization insurance expires. The community

---

Nursing Homes, August 1962.

can ill afford the present shortage of hospital beds. Therefore, the hospitals, the patients and their families, and the community all suffer. The logical answer lies in the hands of those who operate nursing homes.

How do they equip themselves to handle these problems? Surprisingly, it is neither elaborate nor expensive. The necessary commodity is good care of the patient—above all, good nurses. But the services of a physical therapist, visiting laboratory personnel, and someone with an understanding of diet are necessary for properly meeting the medical problems. A physician must see these patients at frequent intervals, because their medical problems are continuing ones. He must evaluate the patient, establish therapy, set goals, and confer with and train the professional personnel. This requires frequent visits. Too often patients are discharged from a hospital where they have been seen once or twice daily and admitted to a nursing home where, beginning the next day, they are seen once or twice a month. This is unrealistic and fosters despair on the part of the nursing-home staff, the patients and their families. Invariably these patients have been seen by specialists in the general hospital, including physiatrists, neurosurgeons and orthopedists. Thus it is extremely important to obtain the hospital records and thereby derive the benefit of the opinions and recommendations of these specialists. These services cost not one penny and mean the difference between the very best care and poor care. The decision as to whether the nursing home will be the best or the worst rests on these factors.

We have been discussing "Why"? Let us discuss "How"? The following are some of the goals and methods for management of the various disorders seen commonly in nursing homes.

TREATMENT

Strokes, Amputations, Brain Surgery, Major Fractures

All of these entities are included in one group because they have a great deal in common. In each case, the patient has been a long time in bed. The major goal is the earliest possible ambulation. Here the physician, physical therapist and nurse must function as a well coordinated team. Is the patient medically well enough to get out of bed? Can he tolerate the upright position? Is he motivated to try? Can we remove the catheter? Is there impaction? When a diabetic becomes more active, can the insulin dosage be decreased? Shall a walker or parallel bars be used? Is the family helping or hurting? Is a short leg-brace necessary? Alone, either physician, nurse nor physical therapist can answer all of these questions; but, together, they can. The patient's improvement and recovery depend upon the correct answer to every question; answers to only some questions is not enough. Although the conditions in this group have much in common, they present individual problems as well. For example, is the stump properly wrapped? Does it have a good range of motion? Is the fracture healing well? Should weight-bearing be permitted? Is the patient learning to shave, cut food, dress, and manipulate buttons with only one useful arm? The answers to such questions *must* be complete and correct.

Body Casts

These patients cannot be managed in their homes, but they do not require the services of a general hospital. They are ideally suited for good nursing homes. The big problem is that of morale. Remaining several months immobilized in plaster is a great trial. Not only are the patients unable to get out of bed; they are hardly able to move in bed. Kind, optimistic, imaginative care goes a long way. Care of bowels, bladder and skin is also a challenge.

Carcinoma

When patients with carcinoma require nursing-home care, the disease is far advanced. We should bear in mind that we gently and kindly help people into this world and we are fully obliged to help them, likewise, as they leave. Too often patients are left to feel abandoned, suffering and frightened. They must be provided with kind, cheerful, even optimistic, attention. Suffering is unnecessary. It can be a result of fear as well as pain.

There are a few special nursing techniques that may be necessary for some of these patients. These include catheter drainage of the bladder, tube feedings, administration of intravenous or subcutaneous fluids, tracheostomy care, and (rarely) administration of oxygen. The mere mention of these frightens many nursing home personnel. Such techniques are, however, easily learned, and in return for the slight extra effort required, they greatly widen the scope and excellence of nursing homes. The following is an illustrative case:

Mr. G. was a seventy-four-year-old retired newspaper reporter, well known in his community. He was admitted to the hospital following a cerebrovascular accident which had resulted in profound right hemiplegia and aphasia. During his stay in the hospital his medical condition improved and became stabilized, but the paralysis and speech defect persisted. Feeding was a problem. Because of incontinence, the skin required careful attention; an external catheter was used. The patient gradually became accustomed to the upright position and physical therapy was instituted. Nocturnal confusion required medication. At the end of three weeks in the hospital, his Blue Cross coverage was exhausted. Mr. G. was nowhere near well enough to return to his home, and not ready for a rehabilitation center. Hospital charges were now high. The waiting list for admission to the hospital was long and demand for his bed was great. There was no choice but to keep Mr. G. in the hospital unless a good nursing home was available. Fortunately, one was. He was transferred to this nursing home, where he was seen daily by his physician. He was cared for by an attentive nursing staff and a visiting therapist, and he made excellent progress. The expense to the family was less than half the expense of keeping him in a hospital. Meanwhile his former hospital bed was being used by some patient with an acute condition urgently requiring treatment.

There are thousands of Mr. G's in general hospitals waiting for a solution to the problem of their medical care.

CONCLUSIONS

Modern nursing homes must be facilities for good medical care of the patient. Families should look upon transfer to a nursing home as something *done* for the patient and not *to* him.

NURSING HOMES*

Ruth and Edward Brecher

THE MANY KINDS OF CARE

An estimated 350,000 Americans are being cared for today in nursing homes and an additional 250,000 in related facilities—boarding homes, rest homes, convalescent homes and hospitals, and so on.† The average age of the men and women in the nursing homes is eighty; many are in their 90's. Their average stay is more than a year; many stay on year after year. Two-thirds are women; very few are married couples. Only half can walk by themselves, even with the aid of canes or crutches. Many are bedridden, incontinent, out of touch with reality. Others, in relatively good health and spirits, are lodged in nursing homes because they have no place to go—or because the minimal services they need are not available elsewhere in the communities. The cost of nursing-home care to the residents, their families, and American taxpayers exceeds half a billion dollars a year.

What kinds of care are these nursing-home residents receiving? How can the quality of their care be improved? And how can an aged man or woman in need of nursing-home care—or more commonly, his family—shop for and find a home of the appropriate type where the quality of care is high, where the cost is

*Consumers Reports, 29:1: 30-36, January 1964.

†The meanings of these and similar terms differ from state to state and even from home to home. The basic distinction is between "skilled nursing homes," where registered professional nurses (R.N.'s) or licensed practical nurses (L.P.N.'s) are on duty, and "homes for the aging," which offer residential or personal care but not fully skilled nursing service. Some homes, of course, provide both kinds of service, in separate units or wings under one roof.
Only facilities for the aging and aged are covered in this article; nursing homes for infants, children, and other specialized groups raise problems of different kinds.

moderate, and where the resident will be happy, or at least contented?

This month CU presents the first of a major series of reports on this extremely important corner of the American medical care and social care structure. CU's findings should interest readers in three separate respects:

As family members, many of us already have close relatives in nursing homes. Many more of us will be faced during the years ahead with the need to find a suitable nursing home for a parent or grandparent, an aunt or uncle, a brother or sister. Few people have even the foggiest notion of how to start shopping for a nursing home. CU will offer concrete practical suggestions.

As aging citizens ourselves, many of us will need nursing-home care for months at a stretch, or even year after year, during our own later years. We all thus have a direct personal interest—however remote it may seem to us at the moment—in the development of a nationwide pattern of high-quality care.

As taxpayers, all of us are helping to pay the cost of nursing-home care for the indigent and the medically indigent (roughly half of all nursing home residents are receiving public assistance from tax funds). All of us thus have an interest in getting our money's worth for our tax dollars, and we also share responsibility for the sometimes woefully sub-standard quality of nursing-home care.

CU has drawn for these reports on data of many kinds from many sources. CU researchers visited representative nursing homes. They talked with state inspectors and others whose professional task it is to make the rounds of nursing homes; these informants were asked what they looked for when they visited a home, and what they saw. Both Federal and state health and welfare officials were interviewed, along with the owners and managers of proprietary nursing homes and the administrators of voluntary and public homes. Officials of the American Association of Homes for the Aging, the American Nursing Home Association, and the National Council on the Aging were consulted. The Office of Aging in the U.S. Department of Health, Education, and Welfare supplied much additional data. Many thousands of pages of official and unofficial reports, surveys, investigation findings, hearings, and statistical tabulations on nursing homes and other facilities for the aged were assembled and intensively gone through. Forty states also supplied data on nursing-home conditions within their borders. Finally, the text of CU's articles was reviewed by authorities especially qualified to advise on the major aspects of nursing-home care.

The Good and the Bad

The authorities agreed that there has been a notable improvement in nursing-home conditions during recent years, and that many excellent homes are now in operation. But, as might be expected, some shocking conditions were also reported. Here are some examples:

Some nursing homes in some states are filthy, fetid, unsafe, overcrowded—unfit for human habitation. Many are understaffed. Their residents are ill-kempt, neglected, undernourished, and in extreme cases maltreated. We were told by trustworthy informants of homes where residents were forbidden to leave their own rooms, of homes where residents were kept in bed, regardless of their ability to get up and move about, and of patients subjected needlessly to physical restraints. We heard of the excessive use of sedatives and tranquilizers as a sort of "psychic straitjacket." We were told of homes where the food was of woefully inferior quality, badly prepared, sloppily served, and where residents were given neither time nor help enough to eat properly. We heard of homes where incontinent patients were left unchanged for hours, and one home where the residents were locked up at night like criminals, with no one at all left in attendance.

State licensing regulations are designed to prevent such abuses and close down the worst homes. All fifty states have licensing laws. Yet some homes that fail to meet even minimum licensing requirements continue to operate unlicensed in some states. More amazing still, some state and local welfare agencies continue to lodge residents in these substandard, unlicensed, "bootleg" homes at public expense. Thus while health departments in these states make feeble efforts to reform or close down the worst offenders, welfare officials go right on pumping state and Federal funds into them to keep them open. "We have to have *some* place to lodge these people." welfare officials argue. "We can't just put them out on the street, and we haven't funds enough to buy them decent care."

A few local welfare departments still "auction off" nursing-homes applicants to the lowest bidder; the nursing home that quotes the lowest rate gets the body. The effect of this practice on standards of nursing-home care can be easily imagined.

Families often turn to the family physicians for advice on selecting a nursing home; but some physicians are not objective counselors because, unknown to their patients, they share in the profits of the nursing homes whose services they recommend. The ownership of a nursing home by a physician is quite unobjectionable and may even be beneficial in some cases—where the physician is actually the administrator of the home, for example, or where he supervises its medical program and his financial interest is fully known to his patients. But secret participation by physicians in nursing-home ownership or profitsharing is an evil, for it gives the physician a financial incentive to refer his patients to the home in which he has a stake. Some physicians have no doubt been attracted to nursing-home investment by reports of high profits— sometimes 30 per cent or more a year—on such investments. Nursing homes welcome physician-investors for obvious reasons. "All you have to do to keep a nursing home profitably full," CU researchers were told, "is to cut a physician or two in on the profits." The 1959 Code of Ethics of the American Nursing Home Association provides: "No financial inducements of any kind shall be offered to any personnel or organization for the purpose of attracting patients to a nursing home"—but this clause is apparently not applicable to sharing the profits of the home with physician-investors. No one knows how many physicans and physicians' wives are involved, since the true ownership of proprietary nursing homes is readily masked by corporate subterfuges. This is a festering scandal that warrants prompt attention from the American Medical Association, county medical societies, and state licensing officials.

Geriatric authorities agree that sound nursing care for the aged includes keeping them up and about, encouraging them to remain as active as their physical condition will permit rather than confining them to bed. Many nursing homes charge more for the care of the bed-ridden patients; hence they may keep patients in bed unnecessarily month after month (with the deterioration of body and mind that almost inevitably results) in order to earn the higher bed-care rate. Other nursing homes may do the same as a matter of convenience. Some homes—including licensed homes in some states—have no place where patients can meet, eat, or even sit and talk except for their beds and bedside chairs. Day rooms, dining rooms and other social facilities either do not exist or else have long since been filled with beds.

Such details could be multiplied; indeed, the sad plight of nursing-home residents has been a common target of muckraking newspaper exposés. CU researchers can affirm that such conditions do exist.

But to emphasize the worst nursing homes is to provide a seriously misleading picture. For standards have unquestionably been rising. In some states even the worst homes provide tolerable conditions. CU researchers visited a number of nursing homes where good care was being provided in pleasant surroundings at a cost that state and local welfare departments were able to pay. This bizarre mixture of outstanding homes, mediocre homes and intolerable homes operating side by side is one of the most striking features of the nursing-home picture today.

HOW THE NURSING HOMES GOT WHERE THEY ARE

A generation ago, as part of the New Deal efforts to end the Great Depression, the Social Security Act of 1935 revolutionized the economic status of the aged in the United States. In addition to assuring modest monthly social security payments to the employed and their dependents upon retirement, the Act provided Old Age Assistance (OAA) as a matter of right to all those past sixty-five who were in need. Thus many who had long been penniless found themselves suddenly in receipt of a small but dependable monthly income.

A Supply for the Demand

Boarding houses, naturally enough, sprang up to shelter these new beneficiaries. Typically, they were run by widows or unemployed couples who hoped to save their own homes and independence by taking in half a dozen residents older and worse off than they were. An unwise proviso in the 1935 Act, moreover, hastened this trend. It withheld OAA payments from residents of state and local public institutions (poorhouses, county farms, tax-supported chronic disease hospitals, mental hospitals, etc.). The purpose, of course, was to prevent the states and localities from unloading their responsibilities into the Federal OAA program—but the effect was precisely the reverse. Some of the aged, the sick, the halt, and the blind were streaming out of the state and county institutions in order to qualify for those coveted monthly payments. More widows—and aging nurses as well—opened more homes to shelter them.

As the years rolled by, the average age of these boarding home residents increased; the residents slowly grew sicker and less able to care for themselves. Thus boarding homes inevitably became nursing homes. Inflation raised the costs of caring for the aged sick faster than OAA payments rose. The nursing homes were pinched. Residents needed more care and often got less. Two or three pensioners were crowded into a bedroom intended for one. The parlors were converted to bedrooms, and then the dining rooms. World War II prevented the building of new homes and cut down further the labor force available for nursing-home employment.

Meanwhile pneumonia—"the old folks' friend"—and other infections often fatal in old age were being curbed by the sulfa drugs and penicillin, so that even the very sick lived much longer. More and more residents survived into the 80's and 90's, crowding the homes still more. Thus was ushered in the blackest era in American care for the aged—an era that deserved but never received the attention of a Dickens or a Steinbeck to awaken the public to its horror. The Social Security Act had provided the aged with some dollars, but not with the facilities or services they needed at a price they could pay.

Then, in 1950, amendments to the social security laws started the country on the long road back to decency. First, OAA payments were extended to the residents of public medical institutions (except TB and mental hospitals); this encouraged the states and counties to reopen such institutions, and to enlarge them or build new ones. Second, the amendments required each state to establish a standards-setting or licensing agency; this stimulated all the states to establish minimum standards for nursing-home care and to attempt to enforce them through licensing laws. Higher welfare payments, together with rumors or enormous profits from nursing-home operation, attracted new capital (and with some of it came new ideas and good business methods). A boom in nursing-home construction followed. Federal loans and subsidies have further encouraged new construction. States have been required to prepare statewide plans to qualify for Federal Hill-Burton hospital and nursing-home funds.

Thus the years since 1950 have been marked by a general rise in standards, a closing down of some (though far from all) of the substandard homes. Most important, health and welfare officials, and to a growing extent the public as well, no longer view these homes as dumping grounds where people go to die. Many new programs have been instituted for the benefit of the residents. Efforts are being made in an increasing number of homes to preserve human and democratic values—to regard and treat each resident as an individual. These welcome trends are beginning to spread through the land.

PREVENTIVE PROGRAMS: ALTERNATIVES TO NURSING HOMES

Health and welfare officials are also beginning to realize that the nursing home is not the panacea for all the problems of aging. Other programs for the aging, designed to help them maintain themselves independently outside of a nursing home, are at least equally important. These programs have been called "preventive" in the sense that they prevent or at least delay the need for nursing-home care.

By all means check on the availability of such preventive programs in your community before deciding that some aged member of your family needs nursing-home care. Here are the main examples:

Day-care Services. Many old people who enter nursing homes might well live on in their own homes or with friends or relatives for additional years if they had supervised care during the day.

Hence day-care centers for the aged have been established in a number of cities, sometimes in conjunction with nursing homes. These day-care programs more than pay for themselves by reducing the number of applicants for day-and-night care homes which cost much more. They bring interests and sociability into otherwise drab and lonely lives. But there are still relatively few day-care programs.

Organized Home Care. Illnesses occur much more frequently, and last much longer, among the aged. Hence they use far more than their share of general hospital services, at $30 to $40 or even more per day. During prolonged hospital stays they tend to deteriorate and to lose their capacity for independent living; many must therefore be transferred to nursing homes instead of returning to their homes. In many cases, they could be cared for at home in lieu of hospitalization, or after only a short hospital stay for acute illness, if an organized home-care program were available, with visiting nurses to carry out the doctor's orders, plus physical therapy, occupational therapy, rehabilitation service, meals-on wheels, homemaker service, social caseworker, or whatever else may be needed. The cost of this organized home care per patient per day is a fraction of the cost of care in a general hospital. The patient is often happier, and his recovery more complete. Organized home care has proved its worth in Greenwich, Conn., Rochester, N. Y., Detroit, Mich., and a dozen other cities—yet its spread to the rest of the country has been lamentably slow. Fewer than 5000 patients, it is estimated, are receiving organized home care on any one day in the entire United States.

Housing for the Aged. Many aged men, women, and couples, even those in their 80's or early 90's, can of course continue to live independently in private homes and apartments. But the time comes for some when continued independence can best be secured by moving to a housing development specifically designed for older people, with the services they need readily available. Many pioneering housing projects for the aged have abundantly proved their worth. The best of them offer private apartments at low cost, all on one floor, or in buildings with elevators. They have especially designed kitchens and bathrooms, plus a central dining room serving three meals a day for those who need or want it. Such housing can be located close to shopping centers, parks, and the center of the city so that residents need not feel cut off from the mainstream of life. It can be built for elderly people only, or as one unit in a project that also houses younger families. Transportation can be supplied, along with work-and-play programs, counseling services, opportunities for socializing, and other needed facilities. Home medical care and organized home care can be provided efficiently, and a very large project may even have an infirmary to care for those who are intermittently ill but not in need of general hospital care.

Some housing developments for the aging are being built with Federal and state funds by local governments and non-profit organizations; others are being built privately with FHA mortgage guarantees. But the quantity falls far short of the need, and some projects provide only a minimum of the desirable services.

Foster Home Care. Some aging men and women, though they cannot live alone, can live very well in a family and be more happy in one; but they may lack a family of their own willing and able to care for them. Programs to help the aging find foster homes have been tried and have in some cases been notably successful. There is need for more such programs and for much additional experimentation to make the programs work well.

Sheltered Workshops and Other Work Opportunities. Two common curses of life following retirement are idleness and boredom. Some elderly men and women, though forced to retire, can secure new jobs in which their capacities are fully used. Still others may live lives filled with family and social activities, intellectual interests, volunteer work, hobbies, travel, and so on. But this still leaves a substantial number whose lives are completely empty and who appear to be unemployable. If left without help or guidance, they will inevitably deteriorate. What can be done to help them?

Recreational programs and occupational therapy can help many. But some cannot feel happy or hold their heads high unless they are at least in part "earning their keep" as part of the production process. With sufficient ingenuity, work can be found for many of them. One way is through "sheltered workshops" where they can earn money performing such functions as sorting, assembling, sewing, hat making, and so on. These workshops differ from occupational therapy in providing "real" work instead of "busy" work—an important distinction for many of the elderly. Sheltered workshops can be set up independently or attached to a day-care center, a housing center, or a home for the aged. The aged and aging can be effectively used, too, in a variety of volunteer programs—listening to children read, addressing envelopes, visiting in hospitals or homes for the aged, teaching skills like knitting or sewing, and so on. The urgent need is for organizations that will bring the work to the aged or the aged to the work (with suitable safeguards to avoid their exploitation).

Information and Referral Centers. Of crucial importance is a single center in each community to which the aged and their families can go for unbiased information on what facilities are available. Such centers can also evaluate the applicant and advise on the facilities most likely to meet his needs and wants. Centers designed to serve this informational and counseling function have been established, though in some cases only a small scale, in Chicago, New York, Philadelphia, Baltimore, Md., Providence, R.I., and Worcester, Mass.

In communities that lack such a referral center, patients may end up in a high-cost, low quality nursing home despite vacancies in a low-cost, high quality home nearby. They may end up in a home that does not provide services they urgently need, or does provide (and charge for) services they don't need. Worst of all, they may end up in a nursing home despite the availability of preventive services, which would enable them to continue an independent, happier life outside.

The Greatest Single Step

To what extent could we solve our nursing-home problem by expanding these preventive services? Estimates vary. The proprietor of one nursing home told CU researchers frankly that 40 per cent of his residents, currently paying $325 per month and up, could live perfectly well outside—at lower cost and with far greater independence—if such services were available. One difficulty is that there's a profit in nursing homes but none in these preventive services. Hence most of the money, both for construction and for operating expenses, is going into nursing homes. No doubt the greatest single step most communities could take toward improving the quality and cutting the cost of services to the aged would be a broadscale expansion of the preventive services described above.

These preventive services, let us stress again, are not pie-in-the-sky dreams of ivory-tower theorists. They have repeatedly proved their worth in actual operation. Indeed, all of them have already been accepted by Congress as integral parts of our national program for the aging. On recent visits to Washington, CU researchers found the U.S. Department of Health, Education, and Welfare a beehive of activity relating to these programs. The Housing and Home Finance Agency, the FHA, the Small Business Administration, and other agencies, too, have programs for the aging in operation. But the curse of most of these activities is "tokenism."

Congress has authorized the programs, and has thus given Senators and Congressmen an exciting list of developments to point to when campaigning for re-election. But it has for the most part voted only token appropriations, and has thus limited most of the programs to a scale wholly inadequate to national needs. Many states, too, have failed to take full advantage of the Federal funds available to them for such preventive services.

TYPES AND LEVELS OF CARE

Even if an unlimited array of preventive services were available, of course, many of the elderly would still need—and some would prefer—the kinds of care available in homes for the aging or skilled nursing homes. These homes fall generally into three broad categories from the point of view of sponsorship and administration.

Three Types

Public homes are owned and operated by state and local government departments. The latest (1961) Public Health Service survey of nursing homes and related facilities reported that 12 per cent of all beds were in public homes.

The public homes are in some cases the direct descendents of the traditional poorhouses, county farms, and other tax-supported dumping grounds for the aged, the disabled, and the paupers. A few have changed little through the years. But some cities, counties, and states have built and now maintain excellent nursing-home facilities—often financed in part with Federal funds and offering good care to residents able to pay their way in whole or in part as well as to the indigent and the medically indigent. When shopping for a nursing home, don't write off the public homes before investigating them.

Voluntary homes are owned and operated by religious groups, fraternal organizations such as the Masons, a few labor unions, and other voluntary non-profit associations. The voluntary homes run by Catholic and Jewish organizations, and by several Protestant denominations, are of particular importance as pace-setters and as centers for experimentation with new services and new patterns of care. The PHS survey reported 16 per cent of all nursing-home beds in voluntary homes, which have these advantages:

> Funds for their physical plant are often donated in whole or in part, so that capital cost may be lower.
>
> They usually need pay no taxes.
>
> They can draw on many hours of voluntary help to provide additional services without additional cost.
>
> They can tap without cost the abilities of community leaders on their boards of directors.
>
> They need not add a profit margin to their schedule of charges—in fact, they can set their charges below their costs and meet their deficits through contributions.

These factors combined mean that the typical voluntary home can offer considerably more service per dollar than a proprietary home charging the same rates. In addition, the voluntary homes are more likely to be managed and staffed by men and women sincerely dedicated to the welfare of their residents without regard for personal gain.

But these inherent advantages do not necessarily add up to a net superiority of all voluntary homes over all proprietary homes. Voluntary home managements, however dedicated and well-meaning, may be misguided, set in their ways, overly protective of their residents, ignorant of progressive trends. In extreme cases a voluntary home may be run more for the benefit and convenience of its management and staff than for its resident. The worst of the voluntary homes have been described by the Reverend C. A. Becker—administrator of a church-associated nursing home in Wisconsin—as "mausoleums of the living dead, a disgrace to church and God himself." When shopping, accordingly, it is well to judge each home—public, voluntary, or proprietary—strictly on its merits rather than on the motives of its owners or sponsors.

Proprietary homes are owned and operated for a profit by individuals, partnerships, and corporations. The PHS survey reported that 72 per cent of all nursing-home beds were in these proprietary homes. They have gained this enormous numerical lead over public and voluntary homes in part because the profits of nursing-home operation have attracted many new investors, but in part also because our cities, states, counties, and voluntary organizations have been slow to assume responsibility and to seize opportunity.

The proprietary homes vary enormously from one another. Many are literally "homes"—private houses that have been converted to nursing-home use, staffed by a widow or couple who take in half a dozen aged residents, with or without the help of a nurse or two. Sometimes the proprietress is herself a registered or a practical nurse. At the other extreme are strictly modern 100-or-more-bed proprietary homes, with motel-like architecture and fifty or more employees, often part of a corporate chain of similar homes. Some proprietary homes serve primarily or exclusively welfare recipients; in effect, they are contractors providing service to a state, county, or city. Others serve primarily or exclusively residents with private means; their charges are likely to run higher than those of the welfare homes—from $325 per month to $500 or even $750.

Three Levels

Nursing homes and related facilities also vary widely with respect to the type and extent of services they offer. Many classifications have been proposed, and many states have developed their own classification system. One of the simplest is a Public Health Service classification, which recognizes three levels of care:

Residential care, defined as "primarily room and board, with limited services as laundry, personal courtesies such as occasional help with correspondence and shopping, and a helping hand. . .''

Personal care, defined as room and board plus personal services such as help in walking and getting into and out of bed; assistance in bathing, dressing, and feeding; preparation of a special diet (diabetic, low-salt, low-fat, high-protein, etc.) ; and supervision over medication (such as pills) that can be self-administered.

Skilled nursing care, defined as room and board plus "those nursing services and procedures employed in caring for the sick which require training, judgement, technical knowledge, and skills, beyond those the untrained person possesses." Staff includes registered professional nurses (R.N.'s) or licensed practical nurses (L.P.N.'s) or both. Some large skilled nursing homes provide an x-ray department, laboratory diagnostic facilities, and almost everything else (short of major surgery) needed for care of the ill. Some smaller homes secure these services through arrangements with a nearby hospital.

Combination Homes

The Public Health Service also recognizes combination homes —those that give primarily residential or personal care but with skilled nursing care available when needed. The homes in the 1961 PHS survey were distributed by type as follows:

Residential care homes without skilled nursing	34,600 beds
Residential care homes with skilled nursing	12,400
Personal care homes without skilled nursing	124,000
Personal care homes with skilled nursing	83,100
Skilled nursing care homes	338,700
Total beds	592,800

The trend in recent years has been to add skilled nursing care to homes that previously provided solely residential or personal care. Indeed, this trend has proved unavoidable. A home that starts with patients in their seventies, all of them well and able to care for themselves, will find itself a decade later with many patients in their 80's who need more and more nursing care. A resident who must move out because he needs more care than a home provides faces a harrowing experience. A resident may even try to hide his illness to forestall removal; this can make his recovery more doubtful. As a result, even homes that would like to limit themselves to hale and hearty residents are under constant pressure to add skilled nursing care. From the shopper's point of view, one of the most important questions to ask about a home for the aged is a simple one: "What happens to a resident who falls ill and needs nursing care?"

Specialized Facilities

Closely related to the homes for the aged and nursing homes described above are four kinds of facilities offering specialized kinds of care. These are:

Long-term-care Units in General Hospitals. Many surveys have shown that the aged sick tend to occupy general hospital beds, at rates that may average $30 a day, long after they have recovered from their need for the intensive kind of care general hospitals are staffed and equipped to provide. They stay on because they have no place else to go for even the minimal care they need. Hence some 500 general hospitals have established long-term-care units (sometimes called extended-care units) for such patients. Emphasis in these units is—or should be—on rehabilitation procedures designed to return the patient to life in his community or at least in a nursing home. The cost per day is generally much lower than in other parts of the hospital.

Rehabilitation Centers. These are precisely what their name implies—places where the disabled or chronically ill can be restored either to good health or to a sufficient degree of health so that they can live independently or in nursing homes. Some centers serve outpatients only; others have residential facilities for patients in the process of rehabilitation. Victims of stroke are often good candidates for rehabilitation services.

Chronic Disease Hospitals. Some states and voluntary agencies have established special hospitals for the chronically ill, most of whom are aged. A number of these are outgrowth of the old tuberculosis hospitals and occupy buildings no longer needed for TB patients. Chronic disease hospitals vary enormously. Some are mere nursing homes under another name. Some offer excellent rehabilitation services and specialized medical services such as radiation and chemotherapy for cancer.

Mental Hospitals. Though in theory dedicated to the care and treatment of the mentally ill, these institutions—both state and private—actually house today many aged patients who cannot be distinguished in any way from many residents of nursing homes. Nursing-home patients, too, often suffer from mental confusion, depression, agitation, or other mild psychiatric conditions. The newer psychiatric drugs, and new understanding of the nature of these infirmities, make it possible for psychiatrically oriented nursing homes to care for many of them. As our nursing-home system expands, it seems likely that more and more elderly men and women with temporary or chronic mild psychiatric illness will properly be routed to such nursing homes rather than to mental hospitals. The fact that Federal OAA funds can be used for needy nursing-home residents, but not for mental hospital patients, will no doubt hasten this trend. Louisiana has already opened three 250-bed nursing-home units for the care of patients previously lodged in state mental hospitals.

WHAT'S WRONG WITH THE PICTURE?

Viewing the entire spectrum of services for the aging and aged from day-care centers through geriatric housing projects to nursing homes and specialized institutions, what do we find?

First and foremost, few families have access to all of the facilities and services we have been describing. Thus aged residents must make do with whatever bits and pieces of a coherent program which happen to be available locally.

Second, the *quantity* of service is grossly inadequate to the need. If all the states were to be as well supplied with long-term-case beds as the five leading states, an additional 500,000 beds would be required.

Third, the *quality* of service, especially nursing-home service, is still substandard in many respects. State standards for licensure, though slowly rising, are still too low in most states.

Finally, coordination is lacking—the kind of coordination that would channel both public and private funds into the most urgently needed services and would also offer to each person the kinds of services he needs. At present the distribution of services is haphazard, not only from community to community but also within each community. One indigent patient ends up in the understaffed, underequipped back ward of a state mental hospital; a neighbor in precisely the same mental, physical, and economic position goes to a substandard nursing home; a third is fortunate enough to be routed to a first-rate nursing home where he lives out his life in comfort or gets the kind of rehabilitation service he needs to return to his own home. Similarly, a patient with adequate financial resources may get outstanding care at $300 or $400 a month, or may waste his life savings lying in bed in a modern, plate-glass, $750-a-month snakepit.

SERVICE TAILORED TO NEED*

Lawrence J. Rossi, M.D.

Less than six months after I had established a part time office as a general practitioner in Hopedale, Illinois, a rural community of 500 population, I felt so inadequate as a doctor because of the lack of hospital and medical facilities that I decided to speak my mind freely and then close my office.

No one was more surprised than I when, after mentioning the need for a hospital, the community leaders demonstrated enthusiasm for the idea and wanted to do something about it.

TOWN HALL MEETING

So, in December 1953, we had a meeting at Town Hall. About 100 persons were present. The architect, my lawyer, several ministers, two sympathetic colleagues and construction representatives were also there. We discussed the matter openly and answered a lot of questions. A committee selected at this meeting began its work two days later selling bonds to raise the money for construction of the hospital.

The community saw a need and responded. We went from an idea to a complete hospital in less than sixteen months! No government aid, no high powered fund drive—no large gifts from industry. This was a community enterprise accomplished with local talent and private funds invested by local people who needed and wanted a hospital and decided to do the job themselves.

The hospital has twenty beds and six bassinets. It is of fireproof brick masonry construction. It has general hospital facilities including surgery, maternity, emergency room, x-ray, laboratory,

---

*Nursing Homes, July 1962.

blood bank, pharmacy, with a full time pharmacist, rehabilitation and physical medicine department with a physiatrist in charge, dentist and doctor's office in the hospital. At present, we have eight staff physicians in attendance from the area and over forty consultant specialists from nearby large cities.

ALWAYS IN BLACK

Financially, the hospital has always operated in the black. Last year we showed more net profit than some institutions in our area that are over ten times our size—and our charge for services is the same or lower than that of the larger institutions I refer to.

After the hospital had been in operation about one year, we noted among other things that we needed a residence for nurses. The need for a nurses' residence was obvious. Adequate housing for unmarried nurses just didn't exist in this little country town. It was a relatively simple matter to get the job done. Money was borrowed from a savings and loan association. Some donated labor and private financing supplied the remainder. The furnishings were donated by a grateful lady. We broke ground in February 1957 and dedicated the residence in October of the same year.

The nurses' residence is of fireproof brick masonry construction and features a large living room and kitchen-dining area, three double bedrooms, two baths, laundry and storage room. It accommodates six nurses.

At the end of our first year of hospital operation, we also noted that patients just weren't leaving. They stayed and stayed and stayed. Doctors were complaining that beds weren't available. The ancillary facilities—laboratory, x-ray, pharmacy, all showed decline in income, yet the hospital beds were almost always occupied.

BEDS FILLED

What was happening was that patients with chronic illness had finally filled our beds. These patients needed nursing care to be sure, but they needed little else, and consequently, here was a facility equipped to render complete hospital care with expensive equipment and personnel standing by, but seeing little use.

Nobody was busy except the floor nurses. A chronic illness facility appeared to be the answer to this problem.

And so it was, that in December of 1957, just two months after dedicating the nurses' residence, we broke ground for a new forty bed nursing home. We dedicated the nursing home a year later, in December 1958, and accepted our first patient in January 1959.

Private financing built the nursing home too. We sold certificates for $750 each redeemable for $1000 in care as stipulated monthly rate per certificate or payable in cash at face value in twenty years. This method supplied about half the money for construction. The remainder was borrowed from a savings and loan association.

Our nursing home is attached to the hospital and is hospital operated. All hospital facilities are available to the nursing home. All medical care is under medical staff supervision. Patients are cared for by their personal physician. A staff physician is assigned on a rotation basis to patients who do not have an attending physician. This arrangement makes possible complete hospital care at nursing home rates which, in our case, is about 65 per cent lower than hospital rates.

NURSING HOMES

The nursing home is of fireproof brick masonry construction, has large private and two bed rooms—all with bath. The hospital wing has electric beds and piped in oxygen. The nursing staff includes six R.N's one L.P.N., one G.N., thirteen aides. A full time registered physical therapist, a rehabilitation nurse, two aides and the physician physiatrist are available to the nursing home as well as the hospital.

Not too long after opening of the nursing home, we noted that some elderly residents were there simply because they were old and alone and had no place else to go. These people do not belong among the ailing and the dying in a nursing home. Nor should they pay for nursing care which they do not need, or occupy a bed intended for someone who is ill.

How inadequate the nursing home can be for the aged was

vividly pointed out to me one day when we admitted an elderly couple that celebrated their sixty-fifth wedding anniversary in our home a few weeks after their arrival. They spoke German when they didn't want anyone to know what they were saying, and as I approached them they were standing in the doorway of their room carrying on in no uncertain terms. They had refused to enter unless a situation was to be corrected immediately. The situation? They wanted to know why there was no double bed in the room! They had never slept apart in their sixty-five years of marriage. We compromised by placing the two single beds together. They accepted.

HOW OLD IS OLD?

How old is old? You may ask. Here is another example of an old timer that doesn't belong in a nursing home among the ailing and the dying: A farmer, aged eighty-eight, had been admitted to the hospital for the first time in his lifetime and was to undergo oral surgery the following day. I visited him the evening before surgery to determine what shape he was in for a general anesthetic. Grandpa was a real Prussian; he was sitting up in bed stroking his walrus mustache and he was surrounded by all relatives that could possibly cram into the room. Mama, the boys, everybody was there. After all, they thought this was surely the end of the road for grandpa and they were trying to render all the re-assurance possible. Taking a routine history, I was probing for evidence of heart failure and respiratory disease, so I asked "Do your feet and ankles ever swell?" "Nope," he said and then looked around at mama and smiled. "Do you ever get short of breath?" I asked. He looked at mama, then gave me a quizzical smile and said "Ya! Ven I rrrun!" I don't have to tell you he did all right and went home two days after surgery.

We decided that a separate residence for elderly people was the only solution if they were to be removed from a nursing home atmosphere. We broke ground for such a residence in August 1960 and dedicated it June 11, 1961—three months ahead of schedule. Our first resident moved in on July 6th. The cost to the resident is about half that of nursing home care.

FINANCING SIMPLE

Financing was simple. We refinanced all the complex proper-
ties and came up with enough money to cover the entire cost of
construction. Again, the money was supplied by a savings and
loan association. The entire job was accomplished with private
funds.

Briefly stated, our residence for the elderly is simply a place to
live! It is a residence—not an institution. Completely fireproof and
of brick masonry construction, it has many features: Private en-
trance for each unit, air conditioning with individual thermostat
control, wall to wall carpeting, tiled bath and shower, emergency
intercom to the hospital, large parlor and dining room, barber
shop, beauty shop, hobby and crafts room, a full time activities
director and outside recreation facilities. There are four apartments and eighteen single room units.

The atmosphere in Hopedale House, our residence for elderly
people, is contagious. Everyone is gay and smiling. Dignity and
independence stimulate elderly people in a manner that cannot
be put into words. We have proof of this. You could not believe
it unless you see it. We consider this project our greatest accomplishment.

You have heard a report of what was done in a small country
town by some determined old-fashioned Americans. Our entire
endeavor evolved from only one consideration, and that is the
welfare of the individual. We learned by experience. We supplied
the need as it occurred.

It is our responsibility to assist our community in providing
for the health needs of its citizens as well as churches, schools, and
recreational facilities. It is the responsibility of private enterprise
to allocate a portion of its investment capital for these communities who are willing to solve their own problems.

BIG BUSINESS

A great share of the credit for development of the Hopedale
Complex must be given to First Federal Savings and Loan Associa-
tion of Peoria, Illinois. They loaned us $400,000 for our program.
I don't have to tell you that nobody loans this much money unless

there is a reasonable chance of getting it back with interest. This, I consider a tribute to our operation; but even more outstanding is the fact that one of the principal reasons for making the loan was the policy of the Association to contribute to the welfare of an entire community and rural area. First Federal Savings and Loan Association of Peoria, Illinois, is a $100,000,000 organization.

I cite this as an example of big business with a conscience—an example that should be heeded by private enterprise everywhere.

Getting back to the incident of the elderly couple that wanted a double bed in the nursing home: One afternoon I was walking down the corridor of the nursing home and as I passed their door, the door was open and I noticed they were both lying on the bed, fully clothed, and had fallen asleep holding each other's hand. I hesitated a moment, because the scene was very touching.

In closing, I want to pass into you a thought that occurred to me as I watched those two old people asleep, holding hands. It may well serve as a formula for guiding all of us who have the welfare of the aged at heart. It is this: We must love and honor them, we must accept them for better or for worse, in sickness and in health—until death do us part.

FOSTER HOME CARE FOR THE AGED*

Mark P. Hale

CONCERN ABOUT THE WELFARE of senior citizens in this country had for its primary goal the guarantee of economic security in a dignified and humane manner. This meant taking the needy out of the old almshouses and affording them enough funds to live in their own homes. Emphasis in the old age assistance programs and in the retirement insurance benefits of the Social Security Act was thus on expanding protection to all people and on raising benefits to an adequate amount. A second objective, quickly developed for the assistance programs, was the provision of some kind of health care for recipients. Medical care becomes an increasing requirement of old people and the physical infirmities of many may require nursing home care.

Living arrangements made by or for older people are exceedingly important to their well-being. The home not only meets the universal need of shelter, but, in the form of the nursing home, it may be the means of affording necessary health care, and it also affects the way in which psychologic and social needs are met. For many older people, living arrangements provide the only personal relationships they will have in their later years. Their opportunity for recreation, creative activity, and participation in a social group depends to a varying extent on the kinds of living arrangements available to them. A majority of older people maintain their own residence either alone or with husband or wife. Others live with sons or daughters or other relatives or friends. However, because of physical limitations and absence of family to care for them, other arrangements, such as institutions, nursing homes, boarding homes, and foster homes, may be needed for many old people.

*Geriatrics, 13:116-119, February 1958.

Organized programs dealing with living arrangements have to date centered chiefly on the provision of institutions and nursing homes and the licensing of these by some public agency. More recently, as commercial type boarding homes have sprung up to meet housing needs of aged persons, licensing of these has also been provided in some states. Interest in developing a foster home program for the aged people has lagged across the country despite the potential advantages of the foster home over the other types of housing for many older people.

Foster homes differ from boarding homes in the number of people accepted as well as the services they offer. The latter usually take four or more people and offer only the service given by the usual board-and-room accommodations of the standard boarding house. The former in a very real sense offers a "home" rather than merely a place to eat and sleep.

Foster homes can be the best way to combat isolation and loneliness for the older person who has no one with whom to live, who is not happy alone, and who does not need bed care or considerable help in dressing, eating, and leisure time activities. A foster home program is a service which can help older people regardless of their economic situation. The older individual with an adequate income may be as much at a loss to find himself a suitable family home in which to live as his economically dependent fellow citizen. He may be at even greater loss to resolve problems in personal relations which may arise in the home once he is in it. In such instances, both the older boarder and the householder frequently need the counsel of someone who understands the needs and motives of both to find acceptable solutions to the impasse which has arisen.

Foster care services have been developed in a limited way by voluntary family service agencies and in a few communities by public welfare departments. Regardless of their affiliation, these programs serve both economically independent aged persons as well as those who may be receiving assistance. In all of them the major job is threefold—to find suitable homes; to place the aged person in the home best meeting his needs; and to supervise the placement, particularly at the start, until a satisfactory adjustment follows.

FINDING THE FOSTER HOME

One of the problems which has delayed a foster home program for aged persons is that of finding enough persons sufficiently interested in older people to take them into their homes. Too frequently householders with adequate room to take in someone outside the family are interested only in children. However, this is probably something an aggressive promotional campaign could solve. Agencies running such programs have found that advertising plus an adequate budget allowance for board and room are the best ways of building up a supply of suitable foster homes.[1]

Suitable homes must meet the physical needs of older people. An elderly person needs a private room which is cheery and comfortable and easily accessible to the bath and other facilities in the home. Absence of steep stairs or other accident provoking devices is also desirable. A hip-breaking fall is one of the more serious threats to the health of older people. Food must provide an adequate diet acceptable to the palate of the older person who often demands a heavier and sweeter fare than does a younger person. One agency has in its standards for foster homes a requirement that the daily meal schedule include three meals and two snacks, which seems to reflect the fact that eating often becomes more important with advancing years.[2]

Usually the householder is asked to furnish linens and may be requested to include laundry service for the boarders. Provision of a true "home" is emphasized, including participation with other members of the household in family celebrations, outings, and radio and television usage, as well as an opportunity to share household tasks and pursue hobbies or light creative work such as sewing, knitting, handcrafts, and so on, when the boarder is interested.

One report of a foster home program noted that, "When we search for the common denominators that make for success in the many foster homes we have used, we find they lie chiefly in the personality of the 'homemaker.' "[3] It is the homemaker who primarily meets the needs of the older person, makes him feel wanted, accepts his idiosyncrasies, and recognizes his rights as a family member. The suitable homemakers in these terms have "an easy-going tolerance and patience, a desire to serve, a humanitarian aim without conflicting emotional drives... (they) are rather gay, breezy individuals. They laugh easily and may become even boisterous at times. They are extroverts, love a good time, and have hearts as big as all outdoors. They are comfortable inside themselves. They have strong maternal instincts. Against such a personality the older person can ease into a new situation without bumping against sharp corners. Irritations are easily forgotten and bad tempers laughed off."[3]

In contrast to this personality type, this same reporter noted that the "meticulous, conscientious housekeeper" is less successful as a homemaker for the aged. "The more prim and proper housekeeper tends to increase her restrictions in order to preserve her model housekeeping against the untidiness and carelessness of her boarder. Then he feels not wanted and tension develops. Such a housekeeper often gains greater personal satisfaction by encouraging dependency... the docile dependent person (being) more easily managed than the more adequate person who causes friction or trouble through his independent drive."

The foster home is most useful for the person who needs social relationships which he cannot for some reason develop himself if he lives alone. Anything therefore in the home which makes him feel a part of the family group, assures him status, meets his needs for recognition, and gives him a feeling of being wanted as well as being useful will increase the home's value as a foster placement possibility. One possible source for such homes may be those of people who themselves are only five or ten years from retirement. Although they have brought up their families, many still maintain the same home in which the children grew up, thus providing space for boarders.

PLACEMENT IN THE FOSTER HOME

Once a sufficient number of suitable homes has been found, the next step is to place in the homes those persons needing such care. Two things are essential at this point if the placement is to be successful. First, the householder and the boarder must be matched in terms of getting along together and, second, the older person must be actively engaged in selecting the home in which he will live. In the matching process it is essential that the personalities of the homemaker and the boarder at least do not clash. Although we are all different, we do have temperament, ideas, values, and loyalties which we share with others to some extent. These reflect such factors as the different cultures, religious affiliations, political views, and standards of behavior which have gone to shape our personalities.

In making a placement, the health, personality, needs, and motives of both homemaker and prospective boarder are natural elements for review. Religious affiliation, cultural background, and social interests are likewise pertinent. These are all factors which lead to a tentative selection of homes in which a particular aged person might be expected to be happy. At this point placement becomes a matter of engaging his participation in the selection process.

Agencies having a foster care program for older people have found it good policy to have several homes for each placement situation, if possible, so that the person asking for foster care then has a choice. After the placement worker has reviewed the several possibilities, the prospective boarder can indicate the home which sounds the most attractive. A conference between prospective boarder and householder can be arranged, followed by a visit to the home if mutual interest develops from the first conference. Throughout this period of getting acquainted the worker should be available to help on any problem which may arise.[4]

SUPERVISION FOLLOWING PLACEMENT

After the boarder has moved into the new foster home, regular visits with both boarder and householder should be arranged by the placement worker. Some agencies have found that a weekly interview with the boarder in the worker's office is needed during the first month. Monthly conferences for the next five or six months may then be sufficient to help the boarder adjust to his new home and settle into his role as a family member. Flexibility in adapting conferences to the needs of the situation is important in this stage of the placement process. Another is to give both boarder and householder the feeling that the agency stands ready at any time to help in maintaining a stable foster home situation.

There are many kinds of problems which may arise after the boarder has moved into the foster home, and it is on these that the skilled counseling of the social agency's representative can be helpful.

A common problem is the interference of the older person's relatives. These relatives, although unable or unwilling to take their older family member into their own homes, may be paying for all or part of the cost of the foster home. Guilty feelings may lead them to be excessively critical of the foster home arrangement. They may vie with the foster homemaker for the boarder's attention, particularly in the early stages of the placement. They may visit or telephone too often, or they may go to the other extreme and completely disregard their older relative.

In such cases, the placement worker must not only try to keep the foster homemaker a willing participant in the placement, but help the boarder and his relatives handle their feelings in a way to lessen stress on the foster home and enable the boarder to make a good adjustment.

Other counseling problems may arise around extreme reactions of dependency or independency on the part of the older person; the tendency of the homemaker to make the older person dependent; negative reaction of the homemaker to untidiness, food idiosyncrasies, excessive demands for attention, and extreme talkativeness of the boarder; and emergencies of illness. All of these, as well as many other problems, make it advisable for a representative of the placement agency to keep in touch with the foster home and give whatever service is indicated when a problem arises. A good foster home program for older people, to be successful, must provide continuing agency service when needed.

REFERENCES

1. Posner, W.: A foster home program for older people. National Committee on the Aging, National Social Welfare Assembly, New York, November 1952.
2. Bienstock, I. G.: A private residence program. *Social Casework, 35:* 299-308, 1954.
3. Wagner, M. W.: Foster home care for the aged. *Social Casework,* 27:238, 1946.

4. For a discussion of some casework implications of services to older people and placement of the aged see Posner, reference 1, and Wagner, reference 3, and Wickenden, E.: The Needs of Older People and Public Welfare Services to Meet Them. Chicago: American Public Welfare Association, 1953.

ADDITIONAL BIBLIOGRAPHY

Breckenridge, E., *et al: Community Services for Older People, the Chicago Plan*. Chicago, Wilcox and Follett Company, 1952, chapter 3.

The States and Their Older Citizens, a Report to the Governors' Conference. Chicago, Council of State Governments, 1955.

Prussian, D. V.: Helping older persons remain in the community. *Public Welfare, 11:*103-105, 1953.

Silk, L.: The housing circumstances of the aged in the United States. *J. Geront.,* 7:87-91, 1952.

SENIOR CITIZEN AT THE CROSSROADS*

 T HE FLOOD OF SPOKEN and written words on health problems of the aged that reaches an average American could easily give him an impression that the problem of aging was born in his own time—and furthermore, that there never was a time before today when the senior citizen "had it so bad."

Hot and cold war has conditioned many Americans to meet big issues with quick action. And judging by responses to situations of great need, a reaction to the senior citizen health problem might be that "there ought to be a law." The American could vote, quickly discharge his feeling of obligation to these suffering senior citizens, and be free to forget this depressing business about aging. It has been said that Americans are suckers for the short cut.

Amid this agitated confusion, the American physician is challenged to provide a program of positive health for the aging in his own community. Can he accomplish this with the traditional health services and the community resources in his own county?

Dr. Russell S. Ferguson of Santa Cruz county California,[2] faced this question in 1955. He was a navy physician and surgeon, retired on 100 per cent disability, when he accepted the offer to become health officer of the county. Prior to 1948, there was no full-time health officer in Santa Cruz county, and in the following five years there had been eight different officers.

There were other conditions, too, that were peculiar to this county. It has the largest proportion of aged of any county in California (14.8 per cent), compared with 8.8 per cent in the state as a whole. (Many people are under the impression that

---

*What's New, 215:10-16, 1959, Courtesy of Abbott Laboratories.

California has an unusually high proportion of elderly people, but national data show it is below the national average; twenty-six states have higher percentages of residents sixty-five or more years old.)

"EXTRAVAGANT NEGLECT"

Dr. Ferguson found that about one third (3500) of these senior citizens in Santa Cruz county (10,000) were on the Old Age Security (OAS) roll, compared with about one fourth for the state as a whole. His interest was aroused when he learned that various local health departments in the state had fields of interest related to chronic disease.

Then a joint study made with the county director of social welfare showed that a stupendous amount of money had been spent for the medical care of only 400 OAS recipients in the first two months of 1955—enough to conduct a program of diagnostic screening and preventive medicine for the entire OAS roll of 3500. (During 1955, Santa Cruz county spent an estimated $378,-800 of federal, state and county funds for its OAS recipients, and nearly 60 per cent, or $225,800, of this was from medical allowances under California Old Age Security law.)

Dr. Ferguson called this "extravagant neglect" because the medical experience showed the high cost of medical care was occasioned by delay until the need for medical attention was most obvious and desperate. He believed a better and wider program of medical care could be provided for OAS recipients with this money; and that a diagnostic screening examination of the OAS applicant and the dependent spouse would reduce the medical cost and the $77,000 for hospitalization at the county hospital for OAS patients.

Why the examination of the dependent spouse? Dr. Ferguson had the foresight to realize that the spouse of the OAS recipient would be an OAS applicant in a relative short time. Early detection and correction of medical defects would prevent the spouse from becoming a medical liability to the county later.

A POSITIVE HEALTH PLAN PROPOSED

When a geriatric screening plan was placed before the county medical committee on public health and welfare, they were favorably disposed toward it. Four of the 107 members in the county medical society opposed vocally on the basis that it would lead to socialized medicine.

Dr. Ferguson asked state authorization to proceed under a provision of the state department of welfare which allows diagnostic tests in a public institution to be claimed against the administrative fund. This is on a 50-50 matching basis with the federal government, and treatment is strictly excluded.

The county auditor was authorized to issue a warrant to the health department against the department of welfare administrative fund for the cost of $25 for each examination made. All money collected by the health department was turned into their general fund and was used to finance the geriatric budget.

The diagnostic clinic has been held three times a week since September, 1955. A distinguished retired physician, E. T. Rulison, serves voluntarily; he commands the respect of his colleagues and the recipients. The department of welfare furnishes the clinic with a social welfare worker; the health department supplies a public health nurse and technicians.

Examination consists of a careful history and physical examination, including routine chest x-ray, other x-ray examination if necessary, EKG, routine and special laboratory studies, complete dental examination and measure of eye tension for glaucoma if indicated. Any medical defects found are called to the attention of the recipient and he is urged to seek treatment from the physician of his choice immediately. Reports are mailed to the physician of choice and the nurse follows the recipient to see that he gets to the physician. It is pointed out that the diagnostic examination is voluntary on the part of recipient and spouse, and offered only to them.

Of the 185 OAS applicants and their spouses offered the examination in 1955, 133 were examined. Of the 133, eighty-three went to county medical society members, seven to county hospital clinics on economic grounds, and six to osteopaths and opticians.

COST OF CARE FOR NEEDY AGED IS REDUCED

Reduction in institutional care was striking; eleven of the 116 processed recipients followed for a year required hospitalization for only 122 days; fourteen of fifty-two nonprocessed patients required a total of 1604 hospital days. This represented a substantial saving of county funds because the majority of OAS recipients were hospitalized in the county hospital before the State Medical Care Plan of California went into effect in October, 1957. Prior to the new state medical care plan, the geriatric program at Santa Cruz defrayed the cost of medical services and drugs in cases where an OAS recipient had insufficient excess funds outside his OAS grant to meet this expense.

The new state medical care plan allows the OAS maximum grant of $85 a month to be paid to recipients in public medical institutions, and also allows excess income, such as OASI payments to be used for "special needs" such as medical service and drugs. About 70 per cent of the OAS recipients now receive average OASI payments of $28 a month. The new plan excludes surgery, dental prosthesis, hearing aids, eyeglasses, and some other items which the Health Department of Santa Cruz county now furnishes.

Under this new arrangement, an OAS recipient with sufficient excess income is sent to a private hospital for surgery when the hospital bill would be under $500. Through arrangement with the welfare department, the recipient pays the hospital bill in twenty-four monthly payments. The Geriatric Health Department Program pays the surgeon for services rendered at the standard CMA unit fee schedule. Formerly these same surgeons were operating on these patients at the county hospital for no fee. The new arrangement has resulted in a direct saving in excess of $35,000 of county funds used for hospitalization; and it promotes the physician-patient relationship. Over 70 per cent of the county medical society membership has been involved in the geriatric program. In 1956, the cost of the program was $17,500: $5000 for direct payments to physicians for services rendered OAS recipients; $5000 for drugs and appliances; and $7500 for salaries of nurses and technicians.

To date, 1501 examinations have been done, an equivalent of about half of the average OAS roll of 3416 recipients. Per capita cost for surgery, dental care, and ancillary services for average OAS roll in first half of 1959 was 21 cents per recipient month.

Complete records are available on 664 of 767 recipients examined prior to December 31, 1957. Only seventeen of the 664 have been in nursing or boarding homes in the past forty-two months. Total time of their stay in institutions was 174.5 months; total cost over the forty-two-month period is $19,966. In contrast, 200 of the average OAS roll of 3416 are continuously in institutions at a minimum cost of no less than $25,000 every month.

The Santa Cruz geriatric program demonstrates what can be done in preventive medicine for the needy aged, if there is full utilization of community resources, and if the various agencies in a community will cooperate. The implications of such a program are seen when one considers the socioeconomic health status of senior citizens in California alone.

The California Health Survey[3] indicates that there are 1,160,-000 residents sixty-five years or more of age in the state, and one in four of them is an OAS recipient. Ninety-five per cent of the aged are living outside institutions, but around 36 per cent of these have some limitation of activity. Most of them have incomes too low to finance more than a brief stay in a hospital at $20-$30 a day, or in a nursing home at $200 a month.

The estimated number of aged in institutions in 1957-1958 was 60,000; only 9000 were in private institutions for the aged; 13,000 in private nursing homes; and 2000 in private mental institutions.

This socioeconomic health status of the senior citizen in California alone prompts a question. How much public assistance, medical indigency, hospitalization, institutionalization and rehabilitation costs could be saved in the aging, if private insurance plans, including Blue Cross and Blue Shield, were to include an annual diagnostic screening test among the benefits of policy holders at age sixty-five and thereafter? Such a program would not require tax-raising national legislation. On the other hand, it is difficult to estimate the sizable amount that taxes might be reduced, not to mention the increase in well-being that might occur in that 95 per cent of our senior citizens in the United States who still manage to live in the community and not in institutions. Most important of all, it would encourage that vast majority of senior citizens who must count every penny of their income to avail themselves of the opportunity to secure the preventive medical care from their own physicians.

THE GERIATRIC HOSPITAL AT EDGEMOOR

Recently, Dr. I. A. Goldfarb[4] said of the aged who are ill, "What these sick people need above all, is to maintain their conviction that there is hope and help." In San Diego County, California, every patient who enters Edgemoor Geriatric Hospital[5] at Santee receives generous amounts of Dr. Goldfarb's prescription and—what they need most—help to help themselves. The prescription is very effective.

Though the average age of the patients at Edgemoor is seventy-six years, and the eldest at the time of this report was 102, a remarkable number of them are restored to a fairly normal pattern of living, and another remarkable number become able to return to the community. Most of them arrive at Edgemoor by ambulance from the county hospital.

The story of Edgemoor cannot be told in hospital terms of admissions, rehabilitation and discharge. It must be in human values—every procedure here is based on human worth. This 520-bed, specialized geriatric hospital was once the county farm. Today it has the appearance of a small village of modern, one-story buildings—a very attractive one set in forty-five acres with landscaped grounds.

Two old men sitting under a tree are sharing a pair of binoculars for a better view of the mountains; they are clean shaven, have recent haircuts, are neatly dressed. Their shoes are shined. They have selected their own clothes; there are no uniforms here.

Another man sweeps to keep the grounds neat. His is no pastime job; he works all day, sets his own pace, and keeps his own schedule. Once his one side was paralyzed, his face was drawn, his speech slurred. But he knows that old men don't always have to be bedridden or bound to a wheelchair after a stroke. As soon as he could drag one foot after the other, he demanded the broom. Another gentlemen is making a garden. And a painter works vigorously on a building with one hand; his paralyzed hand is tucked in his pocket.

The lady who propels herself in the wheelchair has on a pretty silk dress, her hair is carefully waved; and her makeup is just right. She will play the organ for church services. She was flat on her back with arthritis and almost penniless after a siege of treatments in hospitals. She was so morose and moody her children couldn't cope with her. Today she is loved for the courage she found to get out of bed, and to practice at the organ when her stiffened fingers made only discords.

The man lowering the flag has had a busy day since he raised it early this morning. He straightens the library books, gardens, does a little creative painting and weaving, feeds the cats, helps the nurses and patients, works on the laundry truck, and sings in the choir on Sundays.

A smiling man helping an amputee was severely paralyzed, speechless, alone in the world, and the whole pattern of his life was destroyed. He was wrathful, revengeful—a little man with tousled hair, in sloppy clothes, saggy socks. He made rapid progress in learning to use the electric razor and in dressing himself. One day a button just wouldn't button. Suddenly the whole ward heard what he thought about that button—and he knew that he could speak. When his speech was re-established, he got out of his wheelchair; but he had to spend long, weary hours dragging himself between parallel bars before he could walk.

LIFE TAKES A NEW TURN

It's a tremendous job to keep 500 old people neatly clothed. Women patients mend clothes, under supervision; many do their own laundry by hand. The men use pants stretchers and iron their shirts. Such cooperative activity not only brings a feeling of independence and security to the patients; it promotes a warm feeling on which friendships are built. Many friendships are made when the "Queen for Sunday dinner" is chosen and dressed for the occasion. Suggestions and bits of finery are contributed to see that she shines. And what a cherished day it is for the "Queen!"

The more alert patients organized a Friendly Club to help others more helpless. They pay dues, plan entertainment, furnish their own refreshments. Patients in rehabilitation wards treat one another to monthly parties where they exhibit their newly learned skills.

Many pleasures enjoyed by the patients would not be possible without the generous donors in the community who have provided rehabilitation equipment, tickets for baseball games and other events. The Pink Ladies perform countless services. They take patients to the polls, concerts, movies, plays, and other events.

The program of rehabilitation is worked out through close cooperation of the entire staff and with community support. The goal is to bring the patient back to a fairly normal resemblance of his former self; this is done slowly and safely.

Part of rehabilitation is through religious expression. A little old lady is dressed up and wheeled to the chapel so she can sing by heart the old hymns when she has forgotten all else. This affords her lucid moments. At Christmas a ninety-year-old man recites verbatim the Gospel story of the Nativity. He would be unable to care for himself in the world outside, but he is happy at Edgemoor, and here he can take care of his own needs.

During Christmas time, Edgemoor is a fairyland. From the lights in the deodar cedars, the decorations inside, to the Christmas dinner, the gifts, the religious services, the music—down to the last detail, everything is done to make Christmas genuine and homelike. The supervisor of nursing services says that the Christmas spirit remains here at Edgemoor throughout the year.

None of the patients who arrive at Edgemoor has enough money to pay for his care in a private facility. The accountant who is now one of the best-loved patients and a constant source of good fellowship, had created savings to last until he was eighty-five and found them exhausted before he passed that age. He didn't want to burden anyone, and had slashed his wrists. There are two physicians past ninety, a dentist past eighty, a banker who lost his money; and two sisters, college graduates and school teachers. They broke under the strain of caring for their aged parents. Most are average people—small business men, ranchers, housewives. Some were improvident; many used their resources for medical care for relatives or themselves. All are old and sick; some are blind.

REVITALIZING HOPE AND HEALTH

Those from county medical, surgical or orthopedic wards are admitted to the bedfast ward; an evaluation of the patient's condition is made by the physician and staff. If very little can be done, the patient is placed in continuous treatment and given tender loving care.

If the patient can as much as change his position in bed unassisted, he is placed in a transition ward and evaluated for rehabilation, which begins at once.

When the body is restored, the right job is found. In all cases the recommendation is made by the physician and the nurse. Some work is for muscle re-education; some for fun or keeping busy; and some is serious work in which a man or woman can take real pride. Or it may be vocational to prepare the patient to live in the community again.

The patients are in bedfast, custodial or ambulatory wards. They fall into three classes with shadowy lines in between: dependent, self-care, and those who help others and contribute to the general welfare. Reserve beds are kept in each area so transfers can be made easily when a patient's condition changes.

Custodial patients from the psychiatric ward are committed by the court as needing supervision and care. They are senile, confused. They are taught to adjust to a fairly normal pattern of living. Under treatment they may be returned to useful, meaningful lives, in some cases to full competency. Over half of these patients progress to the open wards and have the freedom of the grounds.

Outright discharge of any patient is carefully planned by the entire staff. A visiting or public health nurse follows the patient to insure a successful return to life in the community.

Edgemoor has its own staff of paid physicians, an outstanding nursing education program, an active research program. Dr. E. J. Carmody is chief of Geriatric and Rehabilitative Services. Physiotherapy and all other facilities of the county hospital are available.

An unusual feature of Edgemoor is that recoveries from patients pay over 40 per cent of the annual budget toward the cost of their care. The budget is over one million dollars. If the patient has a family, the family is billed according to its ability to pay. The social service worker carefully investigates all possible resources of the patient. The patient's resource checks are applied against his care, after a small sum is deducted for the patient to spend as he chooses.

The cost per day is $10.32 for bedfast patients; $7.83 for custodial; and $5.33 for ambulatory patients. The food is excellent at this hospital; ambulatory patients and staff eat together in a ranch-type dining room.

In the last six months of 1958 there ware 178 admissions, seventy-six deaths, and forty-one discharges; in the three previous years there were 806 admissions, 340 deaths, and 123 discharges. Plans are completed for ninety-six new beds in an intensive rehabilitation ward. Within the next ten years provision for a total of 1500 patients is planned.

Edgemoor started its rehabilitation work without expensive equipment. Says Esther Kupferberg,[5] "Much of the success was achieved with bare hands and full hearts. All employees at Edgemoor know the needs of their old people are the same as their own: the need to be loved and loving."

REFERENCES

1. KUPLAN, L.: *Geriatrics, 13*:808-814, December 1958.
2. Personal Communications: Russel S. Ferguson, M.D., Health Officer, Santa Cruz county, California; personal investigation: Santa Cruz Research and Demonstration Project.
3. Health Implications of Institutional Care for the Aged; preliminary compilation of data prepared by California State Department of Health, 1956-1958.
4. GOLDFARB, ALVIN I, M.D.: Consultant on Services for the Aged, New York State Department of Mental Hygiene; Chief Department of Neuropsychiatry at Home for Aged and Infirm Hebrews, New York City.
5. Personal Communications: Allan E. Flaven, Superintendent; Esther K. Kupferberg, R.N., B.S.N., Director of Nursing Services; personal investigation, Edgemoor Geriatric Hospital, Santee, California; (condensation of unpublished material on the hospital by Mrs. Kupferberg) .

CARE OF THE AGED...THE PROFESSIONAL APPROACH*

Edward R. Annis, M.D.

Not long ago in testimony before the House Ways and Means Committee, the American Medical Association stated:

> "Care for any segment of our population—the aged included—calls for a cooperative attack on the problem by doctors, nurses, hospitals, social workers, insurance companies, community leaders, and others. It requires flexibility of technique.....
>
> "In the case of the aged, their health problem primarily involves acute illness and the so-called degenerative diseases. In a very large percentage of cases, the main need is *not* for an expensive hospital stay or surgical operation, but for medical care at home or in the doctor's office. In other cases, the important requirement is nursing care in the patient's home or in the home of relatives. And in still others, custodial care in a nursing home or public facility may be the only answer. The point is that the medical needs of the aged are subject to countless variations....."

This is the point that is frequently missed by the public...and by too many of us actively at work in the field of health as well. This is the crux of the matter that is generally unacknowledged, unappreciated...the hub upon which all our dealings with the aged and the aging must revolve: that their medical needs are subject to countless variations.

So we cannot categorically say, as some people are saying, that

---

Nursing Homes, October 1963.

all members of the group we call our senior citizens are disabled or
ill; unemployed or economically poor; friendless, homeless or
helpless; unoccupied or unwanted. The health problems of the
aged as a group are significantly and startlingly similar to those of
any other age groups.

HEALTH IS GOOD

And, you know, all the surveys which have been taken and
interpreted honestly have revealed a fact that might be considered
"strange" by some Washingtonians. This fact is that the general
health of our aged and aging is no different from the general
health of our population as a whole. It is *good*.

Medicine and its allied sciences have seen to it that the life
span of man has been lengthened considerably over the years, and
even now it is being continually lengthened. And more than
that, we have not neglected to consider there is more to life and
living than length alone; we have attempted to make the process
of living itself more enjoyable, more healthful, and more meaningful for our older citizens.

Researchers today are in almost complete agreement that there
are no such things as diseases of the aged; there are only diseases
among the aged, just as there are diseases to be found in any other
age group. Many of the manifestations of aging, previously believed to result specifically from the aging process, are now considered to be attributable to other causes.

Professionals in the health field have accepted this concept,
and they have worked some awesome medical miracles. For instance, much work has been done in the medical and surgical as-
sault on the heart diseases so prevalent among the aged, and a
major breakthrough in cancer is probably just around the
corner. Now, with the full forces of science and medicine turning
their attention to the chronic diseases, some of which were earlier
mistaken as afflicting only the elderly, the next fifty years will see
a marked modification of the ages of death in those over the age
of forty-five. The life span of man will be increased even further,
and the time when a century of living becomes a reality may not
be too far off.

PROGRAMS NEEDED

In the meantime, however, we cannot deny that there are some 17 million Americans who are sixty-five and older, and the number grows larger each day that passes. We who are in the health field, just as it is our charge to care for the health needs of all age groups, must concern ourselves with the health care of our aged and aging. It is up to us to offer positive, professional programs—now—for the care of our elderly citizens.

To approach a solution of the problem we need first define it in its fullest sense. We must recognize that growing old is a process which involves both mind and body. Human understanding, not medicine alone, is a vital requirement in our treatment of the aged. Our solution must involve the conquering of a defeatist philosophy...the philosophy that says the race is over at the age of sixty-five. All of us have seen men who were old at forty, and all of us have seen men who were young at seventy... the sum effect was based entirely upon possession of either the improper or proper attitude.

So we must emphasize that the responsibility of caring for the body in physical diseases and in mental attitude rests directly and primarily on the individual himself; we must convince our senior citizens to maintain their interests and motivations, that they must keep up with a fast-changing world, to mature with it, and to keep mentally alert and emotionally in tune with his environment so he will be wanted and not be an outcast. We must show them that environment can be conquered with willfulness. It is up to all of us to see that the older citizens of our nation are not segregated from other citizens—in employment, in family, and in the community as a whole.

So the health problems of the aged involve far more than doctors' or hospital or nursing home care; we must never overlook the fact that immediate cures and treatments of specific illnesses and diseases are only the beginning. Within the context of total health care for the aged, we must think not only of adding mere years to the life span of man, but we also must make sure that we provide them with meaningful time. They have the right to be accorded community understanding and acceptance, the courtesy of being treated as individuals, the right to be useful and to be given the opportunity to live as self-reliant, respected members of society.

AMA VIEWPOINT

In consonance with the scientific viewpoint, of course, the American Medical Association does not believe that human beings suffer from illness of old age per se, or that they die as a result of the passage of a given amount of time.

How long a body unencumbered by illness or mishap can endure the living process is a question that will be answered by our researchers at some time in the future.

As a consequence, the AMA is of the conviction that there are no special problems of people over sixty-five, except those imposed by retirement, that are not *also* the problems of all other age groups. And this has been the historic approach of the medical profession—to provide the best medical care available to the aged as well as to infants, to every man, woman, and child, regardless of age or ability to pay for it.

But we did not realize until comparatively recently that an artificial barrier was to be drawn down by an element of conniving political minds to bring about a grouping of people called "those in old age." By legislative fiat they created an arbitrary group—entry into which was automatically assured by reaching the age of sixty-five. And by their concentrating on the small minority within that group who represented extreme situations of poverty or ill-health, they presented us with a "problem" that has stirred the nation's interest and feelings.

The American Medical Association has responded to this publicizing its own feelings on a positive program for aiding the so-called aged. It is a program which would have evolved without great fanfare and extraordinary publicity in the normal course of scientific study and events, for aging is a natural phenomenon normally within the purview of medical researchers looking upon man's well-being within the context of the total health picture.

POLITICAL CHALLENGE

But the political challenge of those who would demean the medical profession and the health field, specifically in the area of our treatment of the aged, is still solidly present. We must meet this challenge with the strength wrought by the conviction that we are right in our course of action.

Briefly, the AMA's program covers eight points designed to help the nation's older citizens live fuller and more satisfactory lives. It recognizes that most of our elderly citizens aspire to be independent, self-reliant, and useful citizens desiring no more than challenge and opportunity, and that they do not want to be classified as a mass problem. First, we ask that our attitude toward the elderly be re-evaluated and to encourage self-reliance and independence.

Next, we believe that the Kerr-Mills Law should be implemented and revised realistically where applicable. Third, we must change our income tax laws to provide for medical care expense deductions for the elderly. We must continue to expand health insurance and prepayment plans.

It is of great importance that we realize retirement policies for the elderly must be re-examined and revised where needed. Other points include our desire to increase nursing home facilities, to expand community programs for the aged, and to emphasize the area of mental health treatment.

This is a positive program. It is a good program. But, unfortunately, the issue on care for the aged has been thrust into the political arena.

SOME FUNDAMENTALS OF GERIATRIC PRACTICE*

Edwin T. Arnold, Jr., M.D.

IN THIS PAPER, I should like to discuss some fundamentals of management of the older patients from the standpoint of the general practitioner. Let us consider some problems which are more or less peculiar to this group.

MAINTENANCE OF SELF-RESPECT

So many old people feel they are useless or in the way, or they believe that other people hold this opinion about them. Often, an older person will say, "I am no good to myself or anybody; I am just in the way." But, underneath there is an inarticulate pathos which says: "Tell me what I say is not so; please reassure me."

It is our job to reassure these elderly patients. We can cite their own accomplishments which are still bearing fruit, perhaps in their children, or in the many persons whom they have benefited. Thus, we help to nurture in these old patients a sense of accomplishment and worthiness. Elderly people do not expect miracles from their physicians, but they do expect interest, encouragement, hope, and respect.

An experience which I had several years ago made me aware of how sensitive and how easily hurt an elderly person can be. Our local newspaper had a sort of semi-gossip column which "quoted" remarks of townspeople on various subjects. The only time I was quoted was when, unfortunately, I said there was no use to take much time with old people, because one could do so

*Geriatrics, 12:612-615 October 1957.

little for them anyway. Some of my elderly patients, of whom I was really quite fond, were hurt deeply and I had a difficult time explaining that this alleged quotation was the result of ill-chosen newspaper flippancy. When any patient feels the doctor is really interested in him, the game is more than half won. This is true particularly in the elderly.

AVOIDANCE OF OVERTREATMENT

We must remember that the old person gets that way because he is fortunate enough to have been constructed of good materials, and inherited a good circulatory system.

In general, we should avoid overtreatment. The usual complaints of the elderly patients are chronic in nature, and we do not have to embark hastily upon some supposedly specific treatment for such conditions. Of course, there are acute situations which call for more specific therapy.

I think it is good psychology and good medicine to offer as much encouragement to these people as we possibly can, by emphasizing their good qualities when we examine them. If an elderly patient has arthritis but a normal blood pressure, it is wise to focus attention on his normal pressure and offer such existing measures and hope as we can to control his arthritis. Certainly, we cannot promise to cure it. Many new remedies are appearing which may afford some relief, so we should emphasize these remedies, and bring him new hope. Aspirin, 10 to 15 gr., three or four times a day, is still the standby treatment for arthritis, but the various cortisone preparations should be used to tide over acute exacerbations.

There is no need to subject an elderly person, with longstanding and relatively asymptomatic hypertension, to any rigid therapy. Bringing his attention to his increased pressure will do no good and may do some harm. If the pressure drops too low, undesirable vascular sequelae may occur. Mild sedative drugs, such as Rauwolfia or the barbiturates, are all that are needed, along with a reasonable schedule of activities compatible with the patient's age and desires.

I do not believe in too much dietary restriction, unless there are very specific reasons for this procedure, and unless the advantages definitely outweigh the psychologic irritations caused by the imposed diet. Mental satisfaction is much more efficacious than many of our enthusiastic treatments with diets, tonics, and salt restriction. Most old people would rather live one more year happily than two more years acquiescing to the tyranny of dogmatic therapy, however scientific it may be.

Restriction of physical activity is a sore point with many old people, especially with those who have always been active. The children will say in the presence of the patient: "Doctor, make Mother stop working in the flower garden; it is going to kill her." Mother is obviously distressed by such a remark and noticeably displeased. She says she has always enjoyed working with flowers, and that she feels better when she does so. I always say "Go right ahead with your work," unless there is some definite contraindication. Inactivity causes deterioration much quicker than continuing on as active a schedule as is possible.

There are times when the physician must assume something of a paternal attitude in the exercise of disciplinary measures for the geriatric patient. This usually occurs when the patient demands unneeded medication, or is prone to self-administration of home remedies.

Bowel function is of almost universal concern to the aged patient, as well as to many who are not old. Many of these patients, especially women, have taken laxatives for years and will continue to do so. Each case must be handled individually.

Old people who are sick do not want to eat very much, and the best we can do for these people is to see that their food is prepared in the most appetizing manner possible. Encourage them to eat small amounts often, but do not worry them to death trying to make them eat. If they have no appetite, or become nauseated upon eating, then there is no point in trying to force food on them. A congenial atmosphere may help considerably.

There are many geriatric supplements which can be given in doses of 1 to 3 capsules a day. A few tablespoons of protein foods, which supply much strength, may be given daily. Sometimes, crude liver injections, or various iron and vitamin preperations, may be tried for a while to see if they bring about the general improvement of the patient. One can soon determine whether these supplements are going to help. I do not believe there is much indication for use of single vitamins. If one is deficient, the others are probably deficient also.

The human body does not require as much food as we are often led to believe. In this country, more people overeat or are overfed rather than the reverse. An elderly person can do well for a long time with one liter of intravenous fluids daily.

CARE OF THE TERMINAL PATIENT

The problem of how much treatment to give any patient, when the end is inevitable and near, is one which is ever with us. We do not punish the patient with a lot of unnecessary "shots" and procedures which common sense tells us will do no good. On the other hand, we do not wish to neglect any detail which may contribute to the comfort of the patient.

All treatment must be individualized, and many times the patient himself can be of considerable help. As an illustration, I recall Mrs. D., and old lady in the terminal stage of cancer. She knew the end was near, although we had not discussed it in so many words. She did not like to take even one liter of fluid intravenously daily for this was most uncomfortable for her. I just asked her one day: "Mrs. D., do you want to stop this fluid?" She nodded her assent. I replied, "We will leave it off then," and nothing else was said.

Let us keep these people as comfortable as we possibly can, and if they say they don't want to get into the habit of taking something, we may assure them that they will not acquire any harmful habit.

Unfortunately, in this world of ours, many old people have to do work which technically, they are not capable of performing. But, they have to do it as long as it is humanly possible, because, unhappily, they just must earn a living. There is no need to make their lot harder by explaining to them scientifically that their hearts will not stand the strain of such work, and that it is bad for the blood pressure. The sensible thing is to do what we can, limited though it may be, from a scientific standpoint. Stress the application of the *art* of medicine by giving these people all the mental and emotional comfort which is possible. They are aware of their condition, and they appreciate that their physician and others are not making an issue over what cannot be remedied in any case.

Usually, elderly people do not want to go to a hospital. I think it is good medicine and plain good sense not to insist upon hospitalizing these patients except for definite indications, such as a surgical emergency or a medical situation calling for oxygen or blood, or for necessary diagnostic procedures. Promise them they may return home as soon as possible. When it is necessary for the elderly patient to be hospitalized, it should be for a short a time as is practical. Many people are so situated that they can be treated in an oxygen tent at home, which they usually prefer.

Many old people, with perfectly sound minds, tell me, in all seriousness, when they feel that the end is not too distant, that they want to spend the rest of their days at home. As they say, "I want to die at home." I think this is a perfectly reasonable request, and, unless something constructive can be gained through hospitalization, I accede to their wishes.

MANAGEMENT OF COMMON GERIATRIC CONDITIONS

A common complaint of the elderly patient is dizziness, which is usually experienced on a rapid change of position, such as from sitting to standing and which is caused by cerebral anoxia, brought about by arteriosclerosis. The physician should explain something about this disease to the patient, and then reassure him and encourage him to take things a little slower and easier.

Sometimes, such attacks of dizziness are severe and may last several days. These are most likely caused by one or two things: 1) "little strokes" in the brain tissue, or 2) labyrinthitis, which may well be within the category of "the little strokes."

When the attacks are severe, the treatment is rest, mild sedation, Bonamine, and some salt restriction, as tolerated. This is all we can do until nature accomplishes her own restorative measures. Frequently, such improvement by natural processes far exceeds anything we may expect, and certainly far more than we can produce through our therapeutic modalities.

Cardiac decompensation is treated with digitalis. My preference is 0.2 mg. of Crystodigin two or three times daily for two days, followed by 0.1 to 0.2 mg. each day thereafter, skipping every fourth day. It does not require as much digitalis to control the average case of decompensation as one may think.

Intramuscular administration of 1 cc. of Mercuhydrin two or three times a week is excellent in conjunction with the digitalis preparations. This may be true, even when there is no pitting edema. Such treatment helps to remove the accumulation of fluid in the pulmonary tissues which may appear to be minimal.

For cardiac irregularities, 3 gr. of quinidine four times a day is usually succesful, but some of these irregularities are permanent. If there is no evidence of associated disability, I do not worry about these irregularities. Reassure the patient, and perhaps, give a small dose of sedative.

Coping with the many manifestations of senility may require all the ingenuity the physician possesses. It is essentially a matter of doing the best one can to pacify the patient from day to day. Help the family to understand that irreversible brain damage has occurred, so that they will learn to be more philosophic when dealing with unreasonable demands.

Urinary tract infections are very common in the geriatric patient. In men, they can be the result of prostatic disease, and in women, they can be caused by a cystocele. If surgery is feasible, it should be performed as early as possible.

Gantrisin is effective in most urinary tract infections, and Pyridium and Urised are helpful and soothing in many cases. Penicillin or penicillin streptomycin mixtures are often quite effective. When adequate drainage of the urinary tract can be accomplished, it is of the greatest importance, for no drugs will be curative without it.

Bronchiectasis and emphysema, with chronic cough, are not uncommon in the elderly patient. Most of the time, the process is irreversible, and only symptomatic treatment can be employed along with the best general care one can give in the way of diet, rest, and tonics.

These people do not eat well because they are not hungry, and they may even be nauseated. They are in need of extra vitamins, minerals, and iron. Mediatric capsules, one a day, seem to give definite help to debilitated patients. No doubt, many other preparations are just as good.

Postural drainage can be taught to the patient and is helpful in many cases. Expectorants, such as ammonium chloride, 10 to 15 gr. three times a day, also help in many cases, if they are tolerated. Penicillin, given in 600,000 units per day, or penicillin with streptomycin each day for several days often benetfis those patients with a superimposed infection.

When there is cardiac failure, it is important to detect it early, and employ one of the digitalis preparations with one of the injectible mercurials once or twice a week.

Patience, kindness, holding forth for all reasonable hope, providing day-to-day satisfaction and comfort in general, along with administration of an optimum of medicinals when specifically required, are included in our obligation to all elderly patients. They have the right to expect all of this of us. "Old men shall dream dreams." Let's make their dreams as sweet and mellow as possible.

SURGERY ON THE AGED...PROBLEMS AND ADVANCES*

Professor Manuel Bastos Ansart

T HE MEDICAL PROFESSION CANNOT remain aloof from the ever increasing attention now being given to the welfare of the aged. There are now more old people than ever throughout the world and they are acquiring more place and importance in daily social life.

Nowadays, we consider the aged much more than in the past. We try to understand them better and can help them more effectively in their ailments.

So far as we surgeons are concerned, it is evident that we can offer the old our aid on a larger scale and with more confidence than could our predecessors.

PHYSIOPATHOLOGY AND IMPROVED TECHNIQUES

Today, advanced age is neither a complete nor an almost complete contraindication to surgery, as it was in bygone years. In a great many diseases typical of old age or concomitant with it, and requiring surgery, we are no longer powerless; we are able to act.

Two facts have mainly influenced this change of attitude: our more profound knowledge of the physiopathology of the aged, and the improvement of both our techniques and our curative resources. Both result directly from advances made in recent years in diagnosis and treatment. Thanks to these, we can perform our operations with little risk. Also, we can assess the risks exactly as a function of the vital capacity of each patient and of its possible defects.

---

*Abbottempo, 1:3:3-5, 1963, Courtesy of Abbott Laboratories

In fact, a large number of recent works have shown, with a rare unanimity, how much the concept of old age is relative, and how every epoch and every nation have interpreted it in their own way, and "how unacceptable the idea is that senility leads directly to diseases culminating in a sort of physiological death" (Wilson, Lawson, Brass).

It is the diseases and not the years which weaken the aged. If organic diseases are more frequent among them, this is because a long life has given more time and more occasion to add to the multiple causes of deterioration of tissues and viscera.

To lesions or disturbances produced in this manner, an elderly subject can react with surprising strength, but the contrary may be feared especially if these complaints are multiple and affect each other adversely.

Thus, establishing the presence of such disturbances or lesions by careful examination, organ by organ, is a prerequisite for judging the operative indication in the aged (whether those who are still in their forties or octogenarians and nonagenarians are considered as such). It is by no means a question of making a diagnosis, but of investigating how the different organic systems function, especially in search of possible correlations between multiple disorders, since, as we have already said, these have to be feared most in the elderly.

DISEASES OF THE CIRCULATION

The statistics on senile morbidity show, in fact, that disease of a single organic system is an exception and that minor associated disorders of several organs and functions predominate at this age. However, among these complexes of double, triple and quadruple disorders certain diseases usually stand out which are not entirely specific of old age but which are more frequent in it.

Of these statistics, the diseases that head the list feature the circulatory system, while those not so frequent, are of the respiratory organs, the nervous system, psychoneurosis and the genito-urinary system.

It is desirable, therefore, not to forget any organic whole in the preoperative examination of the aged. But still more important is the state of: a) the circulatory system: indispensable electrocardio-graphy, arterial pressure with test for lability of the latter, circula-tion rate, orthodiography; b) the respiratory function: chest radio-graphy, spirometric measurements of the pulmonary capacity, oximetry; c) of the nervous system: mental and affectivity tests, electroencephalogram, examination of the cerebrospinal fluid; and d) of the hepatorenal functions with all the pertinent tests.

PRECAUTIONS ARE ALWAYS NECESSARY

These examinations tell us about the state of what is weakest in the organism of the aged. But even if they enable us to draw up a favorable balance of the vital resistance of the patient in question, we should not fail to take a series of precautions before, during and after operation.

We should never forget that senile involution affects the dif-ferent organs in a very uneven manner, just as its visible signs vary greatly from one individual to another. Just as some persons turn grey, become wrinkled or dote early while remaining young in their other exterior characteristics, it is a fact that the heart, vessels or the lungs of most elderly people deteriorate prior to the other organs of the body and thus become vulnerable points which should be taken into special consideration when an opera-tion is envisaged.

It is exactly for this reason that the surgeon is above all con-cerned about the state of the circulation in his senile patients. As is known, vascular diseases predominate among the possible ailments of old age and represent the major risk of operations at this age, above all because of the repercussions of arteriosclerosis and atheromatosis on the coronary and cerebral circulations and the myocardium.

If the electrocardiograph and the measurements of the blood pressure do not reveal anything abnormal in this respect, that does not mean that full reliance can be placed on them, since we always have to keep in mind that the cardiovascular system, even in the healthiest elderly subject, is much less adaptable to changes in blood pressure than that of young individuals.

The peripheral vessels are slower in their alternatives of dila-

tation and constriction which usually compensates for any varia-
tion in blood volume. Therefore, when these changes are somewhat sudden they cause a rise in pressure, which is especially dangerous for the already mentioned visceral circulation.

It is necessary, therefore, that operations on the aged should
be conducted in such a manner that they cannot give rise to sudden losses of blood.

THE DANGERS OF A BLOODLESS FIELD

A most careful hemostasis of the field, with clamping of the vessels, even the most insignificant, before sectioning them, character-
izes the good surgeon. But in senile surgery it is a prerequisite. To
obtain it, one should not hesitate to prolong the operation as long
as is necessary. Today this does not involve any risk. It is also the
rule not to use any measure of previous hemostasis which, for the
moment, gives us the convenient (but misleading) condition of a
bloodless field. This, however, may later cause external or internal
hemorrhages when we are no longer near the patient.

Thus, the ignominious misfortune of finding our patient in bed
shortly after operation, with his dressing soaked in blood, and facing the danger of death, can no longer happen.

To avoid this mishap, we always dispense with the Esmarch
tube or with any device of previous hemostasis in operations on the
limbs. This has the dual advantage of forcing us to take greater
care during the preoperative hemostasis and of thus avoiding the
phenomena of passive hyperemia at the end of the operation and
after, with its serious immediate and long-term consequences.

We never use any topical application of local hemostasis in visceral operations.

We have a well-founded aversion to vasoconstrictors *in situ,* to
tamponades, styptics and to coagulants.

These last substances, which activate coagulation, are in our
opinion more harmful on general than on local application. We
think that administering coagulants to aged subjects so that they
may bleed less during operation, with a view to carry out an anti-
coagulant treatment afterwards, as is necessary in many cases of
this age, is both unwise and very dangerous.

SOME POSTOPERATIVE COMPLICATIONS

The operation should always permit prompt administration of heparin and of analogous substances, which have such a beneficial effect on the more serious postoperative complications of senile patients—complications such as vascular accidents.

We venture to say that this medication is almost the only one that we consider effective to avoid these accidents in their various manifestations.

On the other hand, we have no confidence in the abusively large scale prescription of drugs to be used in the little founded hope of "reinvigorating" senile patients.

We avoid massive blood transfusions and over abundant infusions in the aged. In fact, we believe that the sudden increase in blood volume provoked in this manner gives rise to disturbances of a contrary but not less grave nature than those occasioned by a sudden vascular depletion, according to the mechanism which we have already described. We give both infusions and transfusions in the form of drips by the rectal route which appears to have been forgotten nowadays—for any administration of fluids and electrolytes which we consider to have an emergency character.

The precautionary measures to be taken in respect of the respiratory apparatus of senile surgical patients are almost exclusively bound up with the problem of the anesthesia. It should be remembered that, over the years, the ventilatory function and the vital capacity of the lungs progressively diminish with the resultant decrease in the exchange of gases, and in the air reserves.

This is the consequence of the obstacles to inspiration, but still more to expiration, which is hindered by the rigidity of the costal cage, the functional deficiency of the respiratory muscles and the diaphragm, and by the state of the bronchial tree.

Fortunately, all this can be overcome by the invaluable improvement made in anesthesia by intratracheal intubation. As a result of this technique, the greater part of the respiratory complications which many years ago were rightly dreaded and which greatly limited the field of surgical possibilities in the aged, are

practically eliminated today. Anesthetics with intubation and with
the aid of a good basal-anesthetic, or relaxants, in lytic cock-
tails and of other coadjuvants in current use, run a course with a
tranquility and regularity which were never seen in the past but
which are certainly observed nowadays.

DANGERS OF LOCAL THROMBOSIS

These advantages of the modern methods of general anesthesia
have induced us to dispense more and more with the local analgesi-
as which used to be our safest means of rendering operations in
the aged less dangerous, though naturally, at the expense of lowering their sensitivity—which, even in the brightest of elderly subjects is always a little dull.

However, the introduction of these substances into the venous
system has been followed with a certain frequency by local thrombosis.

The aged are more grateful than young people for any psychical
care which tends to safeguard their emotions and to avoid a situation which might be harmful.

Under their usual mask of indifference and insensitivity they
are apt to suffer more within in the form of mental aggressions and
conflicts which may seem more trivial to us. As their capacity for
adaptation is much diminished, they react in the wrong way
(pathologically) to any adversity.

Taking an old subject from his home and sending him to a
clinic causes great disturbances in his deeply emotional life. We
do everything possible to spare the aged this great displeasure by
performing manipulations or operations, that do not really call
for hospitalization, in their own homes and even in their own
beds. This may be somewhat against present day custom but it is
profoundly humane.

By a good anesthesia we mean an anesthesia which has not
produced the slightest discomfort to the patient and which is remembered by him as a pleasant dream. It can never have harmful
effects, even in those most advanced in years.

We have always seen this and it has been widely confirmed. In
this respect we would mention a most comprehensive work by
Simpson, Williams and Scott, in which the problem of the mental

deterioration that may be caused in the aged by operations under general anesthesia is approached.

OPERATIONS OFTEN IMPROVE MENTAL CAPACITY

It has been said, in fact, that an operative stress might precipitate the course of a senile psychosis. And it is a common thing to hear that an old patient "is no longer what he used to be" after an operation. The work to which we refer clearly shows how unfounded this assumption is.

On the contrary. It shows that many operations improve the mental capacity, personality, sensitivity and physical ability of the elderly.

Thus, we have an additional reason for considering operations in the aged with optimism, but we should not be over confident. If the greatest care has not been given to their psychological preparation, or if the operation has been conducted without due consideration and has not had the desired result, we may fear the worst.

The nervous system in the aged is fundamentally unstable, and any post-operative complication, suffering and failure at this age, has a tremendously dramatic effect. This is accentuated as the relatives or caretakers of the aged are usually filled with inevitable pessimism and anxiety.

Good surgery, far more than good anesthesia, is a prerequisite for a post-operative course without fear or adversity in old people. If the operative region is not infected, inflamed, or submitted to painful tensions, infiltrated or distended by hematomas, if the surgical wound is bacteriologically clean and its margins are well coaptated, there can be no reason whatever for the suffering of or danger to the patient. All this is achieved with a careful technique, which spares the tissues as much as possible and which should always be strictly aseptic.

Proceeding like this, without total dependence on antibiotics, we can be quite sure of an uneventful healing. Thus, once again it must be said that the fate of those operated lies entirely in the hands of the surgeon and he is directly responsible for it.

This careful attention to their condition is necessary for the aged in the postoperative periods as much as or even more than during the operation itself. Everything which is done at this stage of the treatment should be inspired by the intention of not changing the regimen of life, the habits, and even the peculiarities of the aged.

We may only contradict old people when postoperatively they change their behavior radically. This rule applies in particular to staying in bed.

This should be avoided at all costs by overcoming the almost invariable resistance of the patients and by convincing them of the dangers involved.

For these dangers are quite real and multiple and include pulmonary stasis, thrombosis, and bedsores. Nothing can be more embarrassing for the surgeon, or for those looking after the patient and for his relatives than the slow death of someone who did not have to die but who dies after all, wounded and soiled by his secretions, after a long stay in bed. It is always possible to avoid this.

In all well equipped clinics today provisions is made for nursing in the sitting-up position, and for getting the patients out of bed and placing them most gently in comfortable arm chairs.

There are devices which make it possible for the patient to perform all these tasks himself merely by pushing a button. But clearly such perfections of modern science are not necessary to get elderly patients out of their beds as early as possible and to have them soon resume their previous activities.

This last rule applies especially to traumatized old people. Their treatment should be directed above all to the immediate wellbeing of the patient. A prolonged stay in bed should be especially avoided even though it may be necessary to forgo to a certain extent an irreproachable functional and anatomical result.

Above all, care should be taken that the old patient with a fracture does not suffer and does not succumb as a result of the treatment rather than from the lesion itself. This makes it necessary in many cases to content oneself with results which are mediocre but which have been obtained by therapeutic means, whether or not surgical, which are as little aggressive and as little inconvenient for the aged as possible.

SURGEON'S RESPONSIBILITY NOT PERMANENT

This consideration and those mentioned previously are the best safeguards for the life of aged subjects treated surgically. They are also our best defense, because the surgeon's responsibility in the case of the postoperative death of an old patient cannot be prolonged indefinitely.

What may happen to his patient after the first convalescence, weeks or months after the operation, most probably does not have anything to do with it. Should death occur after some unforseen incident, which some may consider a relief, others a tragedy, it would be regarded by all of us as "something that was bound to happen."

MEDICATION ERRORS MADE BY AGED PATIENTS*

Doris Schwartz

GREAT CARE IS TAKEN in the hospital to insure that the proper medicine is given to the right patient at the right time. Professional judgment and a ritualized set of safety precautions protect the patient from the likelihood of medication error. However, when the patient is sent home, often he must assume full responsibility for taking a large number of medications.

Increasingly today, such patients are in an older age group. Often, too, they face the problems of adjusting to chronic illness. This, after a period of hospitalization during which patients surrender much of their independence, to a considerable degree letting others think for them. With the possible help of family and friends—but often on his own—an older person who was passive and apprehensive in the hospital is expected to assume full responsibility for all the minutiae of daily life. This often includes responsibility for taking many medicines.

Responsibility for self-planning falls also on the great number of elderly persons whose entire medical care is given on an ambulatory basis in a physician's office or in a clinic.

In a recent study of 178 patients, 105 were making some kind of an error in the taking or omission of a medicine. An error was defined as: 1) a medicine was taken by the patient, but not ordered by the physician; 2) a medicine was ordered by the physician, but not taken by the patient; or 3) a medicine ordered by the physician was taken but in incorrect doses or at the wrong time (when time was a significant factor) or with a total lack of understanding of its purpose.

*American Journal of Nursing, 62:8: 51-53, August 1962.

A cathartic or analgesic such as aspirin or Bufferin which was taken by the patient on his own was not considered a medication error unless it was contraindicated by his illness or conflicted with his overall plan of care. As an example of conflict, Alka-Seltzer would conflict with the regimen of a patient receiving meralluride injection (Mercuhydrin) and a low sodium diet.

The patients studied attended a general medical clinic. Medication histories were taken as one part of a nursing interview which dealt with the activities of daily living of a group of elderly, chronically ill persons.[1] Each patient was asked by the nurse:

> Are you taking any medicines at all? Starting with when you get up in the morning, will you tell me what you take? What medicine do you take first? How much? How often do you take that? When? What do you think this medicine is for? Have you found any medicine on your own (not something the doctor prescribed for you) that helps you with a headache or an upset stomach? What is it? About how often do you take that?

More than half the patients (59 per cent) were found to be making some kind of a medication error. Errors of omission, of incorrect dosage, of confusion in multiple medicines, and of improper timing or sequence were discovered. Especially those patients who lived alone, who were over the age of seventy five, and who were thought by the interviewing nurse to be coping poorly with the general impact of illness were found to be "high risks" for medication errors.

Although these and other characteristics helped to identify the high risk patient, error making was widely distributed throughout the whole sample. Only individual discussion with each patient about what he is doing or plans to do, and what he knows or thinks he knows about the medicines which have been ordered, seems likely to identify potential error makers.

Patients described the sources of their confusions succinctly. One woman said:

> The doctor explained it all so carefully, and the nurse went over them too before I left the clinic. He said, "Now three of these are medicines that you'll only have to take for a little while. But this one is very important. You're going to have to

remember to take this every day or you're going to be in trouble." He even folded the prescription differently for the important medicine. But I don't think he knows that you turn them all in at the pharmacy and wait. When you get them all back, there's no way to know which pills were in the folded prescription. And the heart medicine doesn't look as important as the other kind does.

Many patients mentioned how confusing it was to be started on more than one medication at a time and to have directions given "over prescription blanks instead of pills." One person said:

> She tells you to take this one that way and that one another way and all the time you wonder what color is it? Is it going to to be a liquid or a capsule? When I get them will I know which one she means?

Other patients, troubled by the problem of getting transportation home from clinic or too sick or tired to wait for precriptions to be filled, left the clinic intending to return the next day to get their medicines. Then they either became too ill to make the trip or they could not get the required assistance or bus fare to return. Others, for reasons which remain unknown, evidently lacked sufficient motivation to carry out a plan even when they seemed to understand it and the medicines were in their possession. Still others appeared to say yes, they understood, in order not to hurt the physician's or the nurse's feelings. They then departed in ignorance, having taken in almost nothing.

THE TASK FOR NURSES

The major burden for adhering to a medical regimen rests on the ambulatory or newly discharged patient. Therefore, the nurse who helps him understand his plan of care before he leaves the hospital, in the clinic, or in his home, must know exactly what it is that the physician ordered for him, how the patient understands the orders, and how he plans to carry them out. All successful reinforcement of instructions, all teaching of patients needs to be built on this foundation. The nurse who helps coach a patient must be able to explain the proper taking of medications and carrying out of the other instructions—concisely, clearly, and so simply that the possibility of confusion is minimal. It is the nurse's responsibility to call to the physician's attention obstacles which she or the patient believes will make it difficult or impossible to carry out the recommendations properly.

Naturally, one cannot generalize the findings in this one study to all patient populations and be sure that the findings will apply. But we nurses can stop and wonder: What evidence do I have that my patients understand any better or act any differently? How can I find out what they think and do? How can I help them to remember? Would medication calendars or other visual aids be useful? Are there unexplored ways of reminding patients?

Suppose, for instance, that instead of showering instructions on an already tired, somewhat confused elderly patient, a perceptive nurse asks, "What is the easiest time for you to remember to take this—before brushing your teeth—when you make the bed—before or after breakfast?" She could then write down the time and incident selected by the patient himself in the instructions for taking that medicine. Then she might ask, "Where can you keep this medicine so you'll be reminded to take it at that time?

One thoughtful older man recently reported that he needed a "detonator" to set off his memory in order to take a prescribed medication because:

> Even when I understand it isn't easy to remember to take pills two or three times a day. I get the doc's O.K. to change B.I.D. to breakfast and lunch and then put the pills on the salt and pepper tray. If I or my wife move them in and out with the salt and if the bottle is big enough or flagged with a bright sticker, I'm likely to take them.

Another patient, an unmarried woman of ninety-two who lives alone, was well aware of her forgetfulness, "Sometimes I don't know whether it's today or yesterday." But she guarded against medication error by taking her digitoxin with the first spoonful of each morning's oatmeal:

> For more than fifty years, I've had my porridge every morning and the doctor told me, "If that's what you do every day, then always put the pill on your spoon when you stir the oatmeal. That way you can't forget it." And that's how I do.

That each older person's point of automatic detonation will be different and intensely individual goes without saying. The nurse's role, when talking with her patient about his activities of daily living, is to help him select his best detonator and to build the instructions around this. Meanwhile, she should identify potential hazards such as leaving medicines on the table in the home where toddler grandchildren have access to them. It is precisely in this sort of talking and planning with patients that trained judgment, based on effective history-taking, is used.

Awareness of—and responsiveness to—the human factors which influence behavior are perhaps the most important part of the effective nurse's background. Opportunity to develop understanding and content in these in preparation for deepening skill in judgment might usefully become a part of inservice education programs and courses which are concerned with improving nursing care of the elderly.

STROKE. . .SOME PSYCHOSOCIAL PROBLEMS IT CAUSES*

Frederick A. Whitehouse

THE PSYCHOSOCIAL PROBLEMS of stroke patients and their families depend on many personal and environmental factors. Among these are age, sex, education, intelligence, personality and familial aspects, as well as the severity of the stroke, its location, and the extent of brain damage.

I should add one more important aspect, the quality of the treatment. It ranges from excellent to poor and, in some instances of neglect, I have heard a harsh word used—criminal. Everyone would agree that in the vast majority of cases we as a society have not applied the best knowledge and techniques available for the stroke patient. This means the knowledge all across the spectrum from evidence of susceptibility, prevention, detection of little strokes, adequacy of differential diagnosis, early treatment, restorative physical and psychosocial measures to placement in the family and society as a useful, contributive person.

Some of the citizens of your community are no longer on the street, at the ball game, on their jobs, or buying groceries at the supermarket. They are alive, in a way, but in the corner bedroom, in the nursing home, in a quiet bed at the hospital, or even in a mental institution. Many of these persons should not be where they are but in society's concourse.

Some of the persons who have returned to your community life are not recognized as rehabilitated stroke patients if they have made an excellent recovery. The chances are that most people remember that former President Eisenhower had a heart attack

*American Journal of Nursing, 63:10: 81-87, October 1963.

but not that he had a stroke. Walt Whitman had an early stroke at thirty-nine and throughout his life experienced many strokes until he died at seventy-three of tuberculosis.

Louis Pasteur performed some of his finest work after he had a stroke at age forty-five and worked for twenty-seven years until his death. At that time, examination disclosed extensive deterioration in one hemisphere of his brain. Another outstanding person, Handel, wrote perhaps his most magnificent musical work, the *Messiah,* after he had had a stroke.

Cancer is a known and dreaded disease and some persons mistakenly believe it equal to or greater than cardiovascular disease as a killer. Yet, even informed persons seldom realize that in considering all age groups, strokes alone cause almost three quarters as many deaths as cancer. For those over sixty-five years, deaths due to stroke actually exceed those from cancer (1).

In the past we had some excuse for not giving more attention to the patient who has had a cerebrovascular accident. The excuse was simple, and one word would cover it—ignorance. This reason can no longer be accepted, for today our knowledge of the diagnosis, treatment, and rehabilitation of stroke patients has been immensely improved even within the past half dozen years.

Along with lack of knowledge there has been another rather pervasive barrier. It was a combination of fear and resignation on the part of all concerned. An interesting example of this has been the words we use to designate the condition. I am indebted to Edward E. Gordon of Chicago for the reflection that the words "stroke" and cerbrovascular "accident" seem to imply a fatalistic assumption that a stroke is an unforeseen, unpredictable, "hand of the Lord" occurrence without apparent warning or precedent. Today, we are not only more aware of the kinds of physical conditions and propensities that may be associated with a stroke, but much more sensitive to the early indications of an impending stroke.

At this moment in time we seem to have arrived at the merging of two main streams of knowledge about strokes. Up to fairly recently it has seemed that the main stimulation and progress for such patients have come in the rehabilitation field, which has in the past twenty years slowly built up a highly competent body of knowledge of how to deal with stroke patients chiefly on a postacute basis, that is, after primary medical and nursing treatment was completed. Sometimes the patient was left too long without rehabilitation and it was too late to really help since months or even years had passed.

EARLY DETECTION AND CARE

Now, the other stream fed by the tributaries of early detection, early treatment, new drugs, new surgical techniques and other advances has come along with a rush. We are better able than ever before to combine both these branches for the treatment and rehabilitation of the stroke patient.

We are aware that the brain is a very active organ. It never stops its activity any more than the heart, whether we are awake or asleep. Yet, its active physical role in the body may be overlooked for, "Although the brain is only a bit more than one fiftieth of a man's body mass, it receives about one sixth of the blood pumped out by the heart and consumes one fifth of the entire oxygen supply" (2).

Another facet of the problem of cerebrovascular disease not often recognized is its impact on the mental health problem. For example, almost one quarter of mental hospital admissions have an altered vascular condition of the brain. In fact, psychosis associated with arteriosclerosis is estimated to comprise the largest group of admissions after schizophrenia (3).

One of the most startling advances has been the development of knowledge and interest in the early signs of stroke and the detection of little strokes (4). This information is increasing and, as more data define this area better, is extremely important that the private physician be well informed about this. But, this is not enough. Much of this information should also be known to other professional groups who deal with people. Nursing, social workers, rehabilitation personnel, and others ought to be made aware of such symptoms. Then, in their contacts with such individuals, they can make referrals for medical examination to delay or, if possible, avoid a full stroke.

Those of us in the behavioral sciences—and I am sure it is true of many in other professions—have been disturbed because emphasis is frequently placed almost exclusively on the physical effects of a cerebrovascular accident and the consequent need for somatic therapies. Too little attention is given to the stroke patient as a person.

Stanley Cobb sums up the stroke patient perceptively when he says:

> This common neurological disorder is borne by some with courage and equanimity. Others are thrown into a deep depression. The variability of reaction is rarely a question of the type or location of the lesion, but an expression of the whole life experience of the person who gets the stroke (5).

A stroke is of course always a shock to the individual and, consciously or otherwise, a reminder of a step toward death. Many persons fear a stroke more than a lingering death from cancer, usually because of the fear of loss of one's mental faculties. One can presumably be brave and noble with cancer but, when one's mental faculty is disturbed, one may fear that one's very soul is altered.

It is important to learn something about the person the patient was before the stroke, since it may help us to understand his feelings and reactions now. However, we may need to go back beyond the last few years of the patient's life since his completed stroke may have been preceded by a series of little strokes and this may not have been known medically. By inference, if an individual has begun rather suddenly to change character, to exhibit poor judgment, or any other personality change not in keeping with his previous conduct, it may mean he was already suffering from cerebral arterial abnormalities (6).

GENERAL PSYCHOLOGICAL ASPECTS

There are three rather undifferentiated features to the psychological aspects. First, the mental changes due to the actual brain damage may have destroyed or lessened the patient's ability to control certain brain functions or interfered with their proper use. Second is the individual's psychic and emotional reaction to the severe threat of death and deterioration and to such mental changes in abilities. Third are the emotional reactions to the physical incapacity a stroke often brings.

Ullman and Gruen say:

> In patients with moderate or severe brain damage....the unique features of the stroke are high-lighted, the chief of these being that the very organ governing the adaptation to stress is itself impaired. The resulting clinical picture has to be evaluated now, not only in terms of what the experience means to the patient, but also in terms of the capacity the patient has for evaluating the situation (7).

The patient whose self-image before the stroke was that of a dynamic, vigorous, successful man may find his world so collapsed from inability to speak and from paralysis that the impact is terribly upsetting and depressing. He may begin to realize that while he might improve he may never be the man he was. This lower status in his eyes is unacceptable. He may not even try if the best he can do is to be defeated anyway (8).

CHIEF CHARACTERISTICS

Sometimes the personality changes so after a stroke that it is almost completely opposite to the previous conduct. Certain characteristics were kept under control before and the damage to the brain has now impaired this ability to moderate. This can be especially upsetting to the spouse and family. No longer is the loved one the same person. While the alteration in appearance may be slight, the individual may be almost a stranger to his family and friends.

Yet much can be gained, if one is to help the patient reacquire some of his former ways of life, by information about his past propensities. While the image presented may not always be an accurate one, talking to someone close to the patient and learning what kind of a person he was, what his likes and dislikes were, what he thought was important and what his social interests were, may be very useful in helping him.

What are the characteristics of many stroke patients? Expert opinion employs many phrases to describe these patients. In the chart, they are categorized, although there is much overlap, into three major areas: the intellectual, the emotional, and the intellectual sensory-motor (9-19).

CHIEF INTELLECTUAL, INTELLECTUAL AND SENSORY-MOTOR, AND EMOTIONAL CHARACTERISTICS OF MANY STROKE PATIENTS

Intellectual	*Intellectual and Sensory-Motor*
Poor judgment	The aphasias—
Concreteness of thought	global
Impaired integrative function	jargon
Reduced association of ideas	pragmatic
Preseveration in thought and	semantic
language	syntactic
Inability to adjust to new situations	
Automatic verbalization	The agnosias—
Lapses of memory	visual
Short attention span	auditory
Inability to concentrate	Dysarthrias
Rumination on past	Motor agraphia
Reduced initiative	
Easy distractibility	

Emotional

Regressive childlike behavior	Loss of self-control
Inhibition of internal emotion, that	Egocentricity
is, externalization of behavior	Blindness to needs of others
Emotional lability	Feelings of inadequacy and
Impulsiveness	uselessness
Demandingness	Apathy
Self-depreciation	Loss of self-esteem
Irritability	Low frustration threshold
Attitudes of blame	Suicidal thoughts
Excessive dependency	Fear of frustration
Rigidity	Reliance on orderliness
Depression	Anxiety: general and specific
Euphoria	Denial of illness or loss
Social withdrawal, and seclusiveness	Crying
Catastrophic behavior	

The language disorders require more interpretation than can be given here. The patient may have a variety of problems in speech and articulation, word usage and comprehension of the spoken word, as well as various inabilities in seeing, writing, reading, and hearing. The combinations and special forms of these are many and required expert differentiation (9,20-23).

THE PATIENTS' FRUSTRATIONS

Our verbal behavior is an important means of personal expression as well as a support for our mental balance. One need only to study the prisoner in solitary confinement, the individual who is isolated, and sensory deprivation experiments to see this. As we talk and exchange ideas with others we are releasing our feelings and ideas as well as checking their relative truth with what other people believe. So we modify our judgments and add to our sense of reality by both social exchange and by the feedback of our other senses.

Suppose we woke one morning and got dressed in the usual manner. However, strange things began to happen when we were in contact with other people. When we spoke, we found others either denying what we said or expressing amazement. If, when we wanted to say one thing, other words came out or if we wanted to speak and nothing intelligible came out, we would be very upset. Certainly, in a short time we might think we had completely lost our mind. We might in some panic not know what to believe and when we found we could not trust our senses we might indeed become agitated. Yet this type of situation may only be a part of the patient's problem. His frustration at his limitations and ineptness may be expressed as anger and hostility. He may try to do too much and become bitter at his failure or incensed with those who counsel moderation. He may laugh when he should cry and cry when he should laugh. Spontaneous emotional language may burst forth without justification.

A story is told of the clergyman who went to console a patient. The patient constantly let forth curses and expletives until the good man went away ashen and shaken. When the situation was explained to him later, he went back with understanding and a bit more confidence.

The patient may misunderstand what we say and we might interpret this as stubbornness. Patients who cannot understand words may yet have comfort from the way you say them. There is always a great deal of nonverbal communication that passes from one person to another. I don't mean extrasensory perception but the set of the head, the expressive face and eyes, the posture of the body. So the patient may respond even though your words may not be fully comprehended (24) .

There is the phenomenon called anosognosia, which means essentially a denial, an unawareness of the disease process. It seems to be a combined reaction to the brain damage and to the unacceptable reality of one's injury and incapacity. The patient may deny he is injured, claim he can move his paralyzed arm or leg, and deny or distort other things relating to his disability. The logic of time, place, and circumstance may be ignored (10,12,13).

Stroke patients often become obsessively concerned with their bodily ills and may make all kinds of somatic complaints. Apparently the psychologic threat to their physical integrity makes them more conscious of their body functions and the need to be protective. It is difficult to determine how much of their behavior is a defense against you and the world, in which they fear the prospect of revealing their feelings of inadequacy, their concern about their loss of self-control, that they are and will be unequal to the expectations of those about them; and how much is due to the brain impairment.

RELATING TO THE PATIENT

It is clear that each of us reacts differently to various people depending on what they represent to us. Sensitivity to this may help you understand the patient. For he may perform differently depending on the person and the occasion. He may act cooperatively with the physician, helpless and crying with his visiting wife, and stubborn and resistant with you. Yet actually, this resistant conduct may indicate a healthier and more positive attitude than the other two. You may represent the everyday reality that he is trying desperately to meet and to resolve. It may be a sign that he is less afraid of you, and this may mean you can help him more. In fact, on the other extreme, you must beware of the inappropriately cheerful or overcompliant patient. It is not quite normal and frequently is a facade which does not mean cooperation since the patient stays ill and doesn't make progress.

The patient often understands more than we realize even though he does not or cannot give a suitable response, so it is unwise to talk as if he were not there, couldn't hear, or couldn't understand us. Douglas Richie, in a personal account of his stroke, reports how annoyed he was with the physician who spoke to others in a normal tone in his presence, but when he turned to him spoke loudly as if to a dull foreigner. But, he was irritated most of all with the well-intentioned nurse who spoke baby talk to him (25).

The patient should be spoken to and treated as an adult, even though he may act childish. Our language should have the word "bread" rather than "food." It should be concrete rather than abstract or symbolic, the word "see" rather than "vision," "good" rather than "spiritual." Nouns are better than verbs or adverbs or other parts of speech (9,20-23).

Impulsive childish behavior may be difficult to tolerate. We may have to restrict some behavior, just as we would not permit a child to go too far. But, as with a child, we need to control our anger and speak and act firmly. We won't always be successful but should try to compromise.

As far as possible, the patient should be focused on short-term goals and accomplishments. Some, if pushed too far and too fast, may exhibit "catastrophic reaction," a general breakdown and withdrawal (10,12,13). Self-esteem is increased by small accomplishments. Feeding oneself and self-care in the use of the toilet can be a tremendous lift to self-confidence as is any other certification of improvement or normality. For example, wearing regular clothing when feasible can lead to an important gain in morale (26).

While some patients who have not had strokes may be teased, goaded, shamed, or persuaded to take greater responsibility for performing more independently and for exercise, this method is not advisable for stroke patients who are already constantly hovering on the brink of giving up. Their egos need encouragement not pin pricks, support and love, not therapeutic enticement. Subtleties may not be appreciated since more concrete ideas and reasons are easier for them to understand.

If the patient is too frustrated or if his speech or actions seem to be stuck in a groove with constant repetition, change the task or subject to something easier or more pleasant. But be careful not to openly interrupt him or cut him off from an action to which he is merely slow in responding. It is almost impossible to tread this narrow line perfectly, so don't expect to be perfect.

One of our distinct pleasures is good eating. When a patient is given childlike foods and in addition is on a low fat, low salt, low cholesterol diet, it not only is depriving him of pleasure but such a diet is intellectual certification of the fact that he is very ill and helpless. It supports his feeling of childish dependency. It is probably advisable that the physician and the family not be too rigid or inflexible about diet. At least on some occasions the regimen should be relaxed.

When the patient is in the hospital his activity in physical therapy, especially when done with other patients, will help occupy his time constructively as well as remove some of his social withdrawal. When we make an effort to keep him interested, involved, and participating, however, we need to be concerned about a characteristic tendency to be easily fatigued mentally and physically. Along this line, we need to slow down the occasional patient who is overmotivated. Such patients are, I fear, a bit hysterical as an overcompensation to get well and to escape the dreadful circumstances of the illness. This is rectified best, not by avoiding obvious restrictions, but by toning down their intensity and length as well as by transmitting a belief in the patient's improvement.

The patient may be severely depressed and may need psychiatric attention (13,14). The nurse should try to be reassuring, cheerful, and optimistic and give the patient a feeling that she is confident in his ability to improve. As I mentioned earlier, personal and social involvement, and short-term goals with patient-perceived achievement will help. We cannot, of course, make unrealistic promises for the future. Either we wouldn't be believed or the unjustified promise would result in broken faith.

While the school teacher's role with children is often "in loco parentis," the nurse's role is similarly "in loco familiae"—a substitute for the wife and family. As with the school teacher, she needs to avoid making her charges too dependent on her. If this does happen, it will place an added burden on the patient and his family when the responsibility is transferred to the home.

Not every patient achieves acceptable goals of self-dependence or even wants to. For, in some cases, the disability is a considerable relief and a certified excuse not to face the problems of one's declining years. In reality, the patient, the nurse, physician, wife, and family must usually compromise and this adjustment may not be easy for anyone.

THE FAMILY

Families differ as do patients (27-29). We cannot expect uniformity here in keeping with our abstract idea of a supporting, loving family. Some come apart. Some revitalize themselves into more cohesive units. The influence of cultural groups which develop and encourage strong family ties and a greater reverence for patriarchal authority is obviously different from the typical situation in this country in which adult progeny are soon separated into distinct households.

The reactions of the wife may also vary. Generally we must bear in mind that the shock of the stroke of her husband can be severely threatening to her equanimity. Her own aging, her own future, the fear of her own death are combined with her fear for her husband. Her new unaccustomed role may be bewildering. After all, she has practiced a particular relationship, habit pattern, and a certain responsibility for twenty-five to forty years or more. She is less flexible now, has less energy, and may be burdened by some physical infirmity herself.

The wife may encourage dependency and may overprotect. Frequently it is due to some feeling of guilt that she may have caused or contributed to the advent of a stroke. Sometimes it is because she now has the desired status of a controlling figure in the household. Since strokes most often occur in an older group she is probably past her menopause. In this age group many women seem to become more aggressive or at least not inclined to control such impulses. If she had lived alone with her husband, his care may be too much for her physically or his condition too much for her to sustain emotionally. Some wives may collapse and depend on their children to take over.

The elder son or daughter may have to accept this unwanted responsibility which the mother cannot or refuses to take. Certainly progeny may be embarrassed and annoyed with their invalided father and secretly resent what they consider an unjustified imposition. The wife may also feel this way and act as if she no longer had a husband but a burdensome guest.

Children within the household may react to this family crisis with improved conduct and may mature rapidly to fill the gap of dispersed responsibility. In other cases it will be too much for them and will drive them away if they are able to go.

Sexual behavior is an obvious source of satisfaction as well as a symbol of return to a more normal life. Frequently the patient will not initiate a discussion on this topic with his physician nor does the wife bring up the subject. As you are aware, in most cases a reasonable and adequate return is probable. The nurse may be the counselor here and in some cases the patient may find it easier to talk to her. Naturally, the nurse must be informed of the physician's medical views first.

While the ability for cohabitation may not be lost, love may be. A woman who admired her husband for his many qualities may now have a mate who is weak, vacillating, confused, and childish. A woman who depended a great deal on her husband for emotional support and who expected him to make the decisions may now be faced with unaccustomed and undesired obligations. Resentment and bitterness may be the response. Again we cannot expect perfection. We can hope for some compassion on her part and some reasonable adjustment to this large problem late in her life.

HELPING THE WIFE

You can be helpful to the wife by listening. She often can't or won't talk to the physician nor can she reveal her true feelings to her husband, family, or friends, because of the need to maintain certain relationships.

In addition, one may find that "75-word explanations" of a stroke and its consequences by a hurried and perhaps worried physician hardly begins to interpret what has happened, what is going on, what the expectations are, and how the spouse can help. The nurse may need to give repeated and lengthy explanations to the wife—repeated because she may not always be ready to understand.

Acceptance by the family is crucial yet what do we mean by "acceptance"? Each member of the family will define this for himself. We would hope that some understanding of the patient's problem would help them appreciate their own contribution. The irritability and dependency as well as the physical limitations that may be associated with the stroke patient must be well defined, so that their cooperative roles may be learned.

The family needs to encourage the stroke patient to participate in its affairs and decisions as much as possible. Increased independence and continued activity, both mental and physical, can go a long way toward improving the patient, enlarging his contribution, and improving family life.

There is no need to belabor the complicated nature of the stroke patient. It is clear that he often needs additional professional help from such as physical and occupational therapists, a social worker, psychologist or psychiatrist, a speech therapist, and others. Frequently a clergyman is of great assistance to the patient and family and may, in some instances, be a key to easing a difficult readjustment.

There are other resources—nursing homes, sheltered workshops, rehabilitation centers, vocational rehabilitation, and golden age clubs. In most communities, some of these resources may not be available. It is important to find out about those that are and to work for the creation of those that do not exist. Professional, facility, and social resources do not, of course, guarantee better treatment by their mere presence, as may be witnessed frequently in the large city. They must be used and used appropriately and that means with knowledge of their offering and values. Most of us will have information about a facility but unless we actually visit it ourselves may never understand its function clearly.

Far too often the physician does not make use of the community's resources. Usually the reason is that he is not fully aware of their value for the patient.

LIVING A USEFUL LIFE

A great deal of scientific evidence substantiates the importance of an active life for all of us, impaired or not (30-32). This certification comes to us from both the medical and psychosocial fields. Results indicate that one becomes not only physically more able and mentally more alert but such involvements evidently contribute a great deal to one's personal happiness.

Various studies have shown that perhaps as high as 90 per cent of stroke patients who survive can be taught to ambulate and care for essential personal needs (33) . However, insofar as personal needs are concerned, this figure usually means the various physical acts which maintain our physical body. This is not enough. Stroke patients need help to live useful, constructive, and contributive lives. They need to be taught to live purposefully, to utilize their time properly, to help in the home, to give service to their neighbors and communities, to work part time, to work full time if possible. This is not only protective of the individual's physical well-being, but also protective and essential to his mental balance.

Under some circumstances, the husband with a stroke may need to change places with his wife in the employment market. He may need to learn many household tasks and how they can be done with his limited physical capacity.

Sheltered workshops or, in some instances, homebound employment may offer work and even a relatively modest income which may serve to supplement other family funds to a point of paying for at least minimum needs.

In a recent industrial study the most optimistic employment figures I have seen appeared (34) . The study included a large steel and a large utility company. It reported that of those employees who survived the stroke, over 62 per cent returned to work. The rest retired.

However, these two somewhat paternalistic companies were not generally representative, especially since they were large enough to be flexible in their accommodation to the situation. Furthermore, many of those who did return did not sustain their employment as increasing physical problems beset them. The figure of approximately three persons in ten returning to work is probably a more useful figure.

Generally speaking, from a productive employment situation, we are often faced with a slow, one-armed person, with less than facile speech, with less emotional control, and perhaps with other physical and mental incapacities in a competitive, speed-conscious, two-armed, rather unconcerned world.

Recreation is very important for stroke patients not merely as a time-consumer, not only as a source of satisfaction, but most of all, as a means of re-creation. Recreation is means of reawakening an interest in life, of finding one's old self, of improving one's social skills, of stimulation to one's spirit. It is as much a therapy as any other more technical effort.

One important facet of the problem has been only touched on. It isn't easy to talk about since it is rather intangible. Yet, there is a great deal of evidence which stresses its valuable contribution even though in specific instances its presence may not be recognized unless one is quite perceptive. I am referring to certain human qualities which some persons are able to transmit with profit to the receiver as well as giver.

To the casual viewer, a particular nurse may look forbidding and act like a rigid, old grouch who complains openly to her patients and is rumored to swear at them occasionally. But her patients do well. Later, they come back to see her and, maybe she brushes them off quickly, saying that she is busy, but they remain fond of her. This nurse has communicated with her patients in a rather special way. They quickly sense she is much concerned for them in spite of her demeanor.

In line with this observation, a study of the home life of a group of children showed that parental handling varied much (35). Some children were often physically punished, some never. Many had too much spending money and went to the movies too many nights a week. Others had little money, seldom went to the movies and went to bed early. In some families, the mother was a strong, dominating influence, in other, the father, and so on. There were other things wrong which many would view with some horror insofar as child rearing was concerned. Yet, this investigation was a study of the home life of *well-adjusted* children. The one common apparently sustaining factor was that the children felt a sense of love and security which was generated by the parents in spite of the way they handled things on the surface.

The nurse I referred to may be creating such a climate of real concern for her patient that it gets across in spite of the surface actions that might horrify her supervisor (36). What is more important?

I could give you perhaps another overdrawn example to make a point—that of the "sweet-dispositioned" nurse who is always smiling at her patients but who, in a passive-aggressive way, is always controlling them. Always, her decisions must be carried out. She is, she says, "only doing what is right for the patient." True, there are actions that from an important patient-care stand-point are necessary and the patient may need control, but there are lines to be drawn and honest statements to be made instead of counterfeit feelings and superficial deceptions. One cannot hide the truth for this lack of real interest is seen through by the more intelligent patients and sensed by the others.

I am not saying that you should blame yourself if the patient does poorly. Actually, I am saying the opposite. If you have given the patient your genuine concern—one might even say love and not be embarrassed—and your other obligations have been carried out to the reasonable limit of your capacity, there is no blame. Castigating yourself will not improve your competence but will deteriorate it.

As you know, the physician has a similar problem of interper-sonal relations with his patients and much interesting evidence shows that some doctors obtain more success than others depend-ing on their ability to develop rapport (37-40) .

The stroke patient is a truly great challenge. But, this is what you want. This is why you are a nurse.

REFERENCES

1. U.S. PUBLIC HEALTH SERVICE, NATIONAL VITAL STATISTICS DIVI-SION: Annual Summary, 1960. *Monthly Vital Statistics Re-ports, 10:3*, Part 2, July 31, 1961.

2. PAGE, I. H., AND OTHERS: *Strokes; How They Occur and What Can Be Done About Them.* New York, E. P. Dutton and Co., 1961, p. 32.

3. WEISS, E.: The emotions and strokes, in *Strokes; How They Oc-cur and What Can Be Done About Them.* by I. H. Page and others. New York, E. P. Dutton and Co., 1961, pp. 111-131.

4. U.S. PUBLIC HEALTH SERVICE: *Little Strokes; Hope Through Re-search.* Publication No. 689, Washington, D.C., U.S. Govern-ment Printing Office, 1962.

5. COBB, STANLEY: Personality as affected by lesions of the brain, in *Personality and Behavior Disorders,* ed. by J. McV. Hunt. New York, Ronald Press, 1944, Vol. 1, p. 553.

6. ALVAREZ, WALTER: Cerebral arteriosclerosis. *Geriatrics, 1*:203, May-June 1946.

7. ULLMAN, MONTAGUE, AND GRUEN, ARNO: Behavioral changes in patients with strokes. *Amer. J. Psychiat., 117*:1004-1009, May 1961.

8. WHITEHOUSE, F. A.: Psychological factors influencing rehabilitation of the cardiac. *J. Rehab., 26*:4-7,39, July-Aug. 1960.

9. WEPMAN, J. M.: The language disorders, in *Psychological Practices With the Physically Disabled,* ed. by J. F. Garrett and Edna S. Levine. New York, Columbia University Press, 1962, pp. 197-230.

10. GOLDSTEIN, KURT: *The Organism; A Holistic Approach to Biology Derived From Pathological Data in Man.* New York, American Book Company, 1939.

11. DILLER, LEONARD: Hemiplegia, in *Psychological Practices With the Physically Disabled,* ed. by J. F. Garrett and Edna S., Levine. New York, Columbia University Press, 1962, pp. 125-158.

12. WEINSTEIN, E. A., AND KAHN, R. L.: *Denial of Illness; Symbolic and Physiological Aspects.* Springfield, Ill., Charles C Thomas Publisher, 1955.

13. ULLMAN, M.: *Behavioral Changes in Patients Following Strokes.* Springfield, Ill., Charles C Thomas Publisher, 1962.

14. FISHER, S. H.: Psychiatric considerations of cerebral vascular disease. *Amer. J. Cardiol., 7*:379-385, Mar. 1961.

15. WEISS, EDWARD: The emotional problems of cerebral vascular disease, in *Cerebral Vascular Diseases,* ed. by E. Hugh Luckey. Transactions of a Conference, American Heart Association, Princeton, N.J., Jan. 24-26, 1954. New York, Grune and Stratton, 1955.

16. DAVIDSON, R.: Psychological aspects of stroke. *Chest Heart Bull. (London)*, *25*:38-40, Apr. 1962.

17. BORDEN, W. A.: Psychological aspects of stroke; patient and family (editorial). *Ann. Intern. Med., 57*:689-692, Oct. 1962.

18. SLATER, E. T. O.: Psychological aspects, in *Modern Views on Stroke Illness.* London, Chest and Heart Association, 1962, pp. 41-48.

19. CLYDE, N. P. R.: *Stroke Illness—Help for Patient and Family.* London, Chest and Heart Association, 1961.

20. TAYLOR, MARTHA L.: *Understanding Aphasia; A Guide for*

Family and Friends. Patient Publication No. 2-1958 New York, Institute of Physical Medicine and Rehabilitation, New York University, Bellevue Medical Center, 1958.

21. BOONE, D. R.: *An Adult Has Aphasia: For the Family; The Management and Treatment of the Aphasia Patient.* Cleveland, Ohio, Cleveland Hearing and Speech Center, 1961.

22. LONGERICH, M. C.: *Helping the Aphasic to Recover His Speech; A Manual for the Family.* Los Angeles, Calif., Loma Linda University, School of Medicine, 1955.

23. MARTIN, BLANCHE R.: *Communicative Aids for the Adult Aphasic.* Springfield, Ill., Charles C. Thomas Publisher, 1962.

24. WHITEHOUSE, F. A.: *Communication; An Introduction to Some Basic Concepts.* Paper presented at NRA Conference, Oct. 12, 1960. New York, American Heart Association, 1960.

25. RITCHIE, D. E.: *Stroke; A Study of Recovery.* New York, Doubleday and Co., 1961.

26. TRAVIS, GEORGIA: *Chronic Disease and Disability.* Berkeley, Calif., University of California Press, 1961.

27. AMERICAN HEART ASSOCIATION: *Strokes; A Guide for the Family.* New York, The Association, 1961.

28. WHITEHOUSE, F. A.: *Psychosocial Aspects of Cardiovascular Disease.* Paper presented at Cardiovascular Nursing Institute, Washington Heart Association, Washington, D.C., Jan. 25, 1962. (To be published.)

29. ———: Cardiovascular disability, in *Psychological Practices with the Disabled,* ed. by J. F. Garrett and Edna S. Levine. New York, Columbia University Press, 1962.

30. ———: *Graphic Presentation of Some Rehabilitation Fundamentals.* Paper presented at Great Lakes Regional Institute, National Association of Social Workers, Medical Social Work Section, Iowa City, Iowa, June 27, 1963.

31. ———: Rehabilitation as a concept in the utilization of human resources, in *The Evolving Concept of Rehabilitation.* Social Work Practice in Medical Care and Rehabilitation Settings, Monograph No. 1, Washington, D.C., American Association of Medical Social Workers, 1955, pp. 17-37.

32. ———: The utilization of human resources; a philosophic approach to rehabilitation. *Dis. Chest, 30*:606-627, Dec. 1956.

33. U.S. PUBLIC HEALTH SERVICE: *Cerebral Vascular Disease and Strokes.* Publication No. 513, Washington, D.C., U.S. Government Printing Office, 1957.

34. LADD, A. C.: Cerebrovascular disease in an employed population. *J. Chron. Dis., 15*:985-990, Oct. 1962.
35. STOUT, I. W., AND LANGDON, GRACE: A study of the home life of well-adjusted children. *J. Ed. Sociol., 23*:442-460, Apr. 1950.
36. WHITEHOUSE, F. A.: Rehabilitation as a dimension of health care. Paper presented at a conference on Newer Dimensions for Rehabilitation in Nursing at Boston University, Boston, Mass., Dec. 1, 1961. Abstracted in *Rehab. Record, 3*:9-12, July-Aug. 1962.
37. BOSHES, BENJAMIN: The status of tranquilizing drugs 1959. *Ann. Intern. Med., 52*:182-194, Jan. 1960.
38. COLE, S. L., AND OTHERS: Assay of antianginal agents—the rapport period. *J.A.M.A., 168*:275-277, Sept. 20, 1958.
39. WOLF, STEWART: Effects of suggestion and conditioning on action of chemical agents in human subjects; pharmacology of placebos. *J. Clin. Invest., 29*:100-109, Jan, 1950.
40. ESKWITH, I. S.: Holistic approach in the management of angina pectoris. *Postgrad. Med., 27*:203-206, Feb. 1960.

BIBLIOGRAPHY

KUHN, R. A.: *New Hope for Stroke Victims.* New York, Appleton-Century-Crofts, 1960.

TAYLOR, M. L., AND MARKS, M.: *Aphasia Rehabilitation Manual and Work Book.* New York, Institute of Physical Medicine and Rehabilitation, New York University-Bellevue Medical Center, 1955.

WHITEHOUSE, F. A.: Cardiovascular disease and mental health. *Rehab. Lit., 24*:130-139, May 1963.

OSTEOPOROSIS OF THE SPINE*

Robert C. Lonergan

T HE FACT THAT PEOPLE—and particularly women—are living longer has made certain disease entities much more common. One of these is osteoporosis of the spine.[1]

Discussing pathological fractures of the spine in a recently published paper, Nicholas and his associates said that "osteoporosis of variable degree is usually present in the late decades of life, and spontaneous compression fractures are common at this time. The disease is rare before the age of fifty, but thereafter its incidence increases with each decade" (1). In St. Petersburg, Florida for example, where there is a high concentration of retired elderly people, many women in the postmenopausal period of life commonly develop severe back pain, and x-rays will confirm the diagnosis of osteoporosis of the spine.

There is still considerable doubt about the exact etiology of osteoporosis. Not all cases can be attributed to a postmenopausal attrition, with loss of hormone function—for the disease does occur in men. Most medical classifications include another category—idiopathic osteoporosis—which by definition admits an unknown origin. In his textbook, *The Back and Disc Syndromes*, Lewin sums up the simply and succinctly by saying that the etiology is bound up with bone metabolism and is influenced by such factors as gonadal hormone deficiency, decreased use of the body (resulting in a lessening of the normal skeletal strains which stimulate osteoplastic activity) , and lack of protein foods (2) .

---

*American Journal of Nursing, 61:1:79-81, Jan. 1961.

[1]Although osteoporosis is actually an abnormal chemical and biological condition of the bone, the term, as commonly used, has come to mean a specific disease classification.

There are others who feel that old-age atrophy of the bone matrix is the most important single causative factor in the disease. However, x-rays of osteoporotic spines clearly show demineralization, thinning of cortical bone, and changes in the contour of the vertebrae.

THE CLINICAL PICTURE

Compression fractures, often multiple, frequently are present, and the resulting wedge-shaped vertebrae produce a severe dorsal hump-backed deformity with a shortening of the thorax, and a corresponding loss of stature. In the lumbar spine the vertebrae, with their structural weakness, suffer from the expansile force of the intervertebral discs and develop biconcave depressions of their surfaces. The total result of these changes is an over-all deformity of the spine, and the stress effect is undoubtedly the cause of severe back pain. It is the back pain, coinciding probably with the occurrence of spontaneous fractures, that forces the individual to seek medical attention.

In establishing the diagnosis, it is important to rule out such conditions as metastatic malignant disease, acute trauma, and demineralization due to long, continued treatment by the corticosteroid drugs. Careful clinical study is necessary for differentiation.

The following case history illustrates many of the facets, symptoms, and signs of osteoporosis and emphasizes some of its important features, including the fact that the disease is much more common in women than in men.

Mrs. White, a seventy-year-old woman, had been having severe mid- and low-back pain for three months.

Present illness.—The onset of the acute symptoms followed a minor incident. For a period of two hours the patient had been bending over and edging a small grass plot around the trailer in which she lived. She noticed minor back distress after this chore, but the discomfort was not severe. On the following day she continued the job until the pain became so severe that she stopped her work and consulted a physician. Hospitalization was recommended and she was treated for a period of two weeks. Following discharge, however, the symptoms did not subside, and within a few days she returned to the hospital for further treatment.

Past History. There was remarkably little of importance in the patient's past medical history except for a hysterectomy that had been performed many years before. Her general health had always been excellent, and she denied having any critical illness or systematic disease.

Physical Examination. Examination by a medical consultant revealed the expected body changes of an elderly woman, but there were no gross functional deficiencies. From her history, we suspected that she had had a mild cardiac insufficiency but this was not confirmed by the clinical findings. Rectal examination was negative; pelvic examination confirmed the prior hysterectomy.

Laboratory Findings. A blood count revealed a PCV (Packed Cell Volume) of 39 per cent; hemoglobin of 11.8 Gm.; 4,170,000 red blood cells; 6250 white blood cells. The differential was normal; the sedimentation rate normal; the urinalysis and blood chemistry both within entirely normal limits.

Orthopedic Examination. The patient was a short woman, with a marked dorsal kyphosis. She was found to have exquisite tenderness over the mid- and low-dorsal spine and in the lumbar spine. Motions of the back were restricted by pain.

A lateral x-ray of the dorsal spine revealed compression fractures in vertebrae 7, 8, 9. In the lumbar spine, the characteristic cod-fish type of vertebrae with bilateral concavity was observed. There was severe over-all decalcification of the spine. Fortunately, x-rays taken about a year before the present examination were available for comparison; and while the earlier films showed moderate demineralization, with some evidence of osteoarthritis in the mid-dorsal spine, the wedged compressed dorsal vertebrae and the biconcave lumbar vertebrae were not present. Thus the present advanced bone changes could be assumed to have occurred within a period of a year.

Progress. The patient's progress in the hospital was slow, but she improved steadily. She received hot packs to the back twice daily, and she spent the major part of the time in bed. Toward the end of her hospital stay, a modified Taylor back brace was applied once the brace was properly adjusted, the patient was permitted out of bed for short periods of time. These intervals were gradually increased until she was able to resume normal activity. In follow-up office visits after her discharge from the hospital, she continued to show improvement and had no recurrence of the severe back pain.

The modified Taylor back brace, which is often used for support, should not be a permanent fixture. Most of these patients get well, in the sense that they are relieved of their acute back distress even though the deformity remains, and while some form of back support is advisable, the rigid metal brace should be removed after four to six months.

In another almost identical case, a woman sixty-five years of age developed the kyphotic deformity even more rapidly, and her symptoms were at first diagnosed erroneously as rheumatoid arthritis. She was treated by massive and continued doses of corticosteroid drugs; the condition speedily worsened until she could sleep only in a contour type of chair. Here the need for differential diagnosis was the first consideration, and a complete and careful study was needed to rule out malignancy. In an article on drug treatment for rheumatic diseases, Scully makes this statement: "With steroids, and particularly in the old age groups, spontaneous fractures resulting from iatrogenic osteoporosis have become increasingly more frequent and must constitute a matter of prime and grave concern to the physician . . . ." (3).

TREATMENT PROGRAM

It is certainly fortunate that the majority of the patients with osteoporosis of the spine can be relieved of their back pain by simple measures. Bed rest in the hospital is the most effective single measure, and physical therapy is used to a limited extent—chiefly in the form of hot fomentations to relieve the pain while the patient is in bed. Other forms of physical therapy have not been helpful; it is difficult to get these old people to tolerate or perform exercises. It is sufficient to relieve their pain, and get them out of bed, on their feet and walking.

Before the patient is permitted out of bed, some type of support is essential, whether it be a plaster cast, a metal frame back brace, or a corset with heavy metal stays. Choice depends on a variety of circumstances—body form, the degree of pain and disability, and, more often than not, the patient's acceptance of the support.

Frequently, the thought of wearing a cast may seem repugnant, an insurmountable burden, to a particular patient, and a compromise is necessary. In these elderly people, some thought must be given to their feebleness or general weakness, and the choice of the support may make the difference between success and failure. Such was the case with Mrs. White whose case history has been reported. Her first hospital treatment was a failure because the period of bed rest was too short, and afterward she refused to wear the brace prescribed—for a good reason. It was not high enough nor properly adjusted.

Some cases of osteoporosis, perhaps more than 50 per cent, according to Nicholas and Wilson, respond favorably to the use of hormone therapy (4). Most conservative physicians use preparations in which vitamins, minerals, and small amounts of estrogenic and androgenic hormone are combined. These preparations are used over a long period of time. Eldec and Mediatric capsules, for example, are both given for three-week periods, followed by one week off the medication, and then three weeks on again, and so on.

In cases of very severe involvement, the stronger estrogen-androgen-vitamin C preparation, Formatrix tablets, can be used daily, again for only twenty-one days with a week's rest, or Depo-Testosterone, a long-acting androgen in cotton seed oil can be given parenterally twice a month. Both of these latter two drugs are highly stimulating to gonadal function and should be used only for a short time during an acute episode; after that use of the milder estrogens and androgens can be resumed and kept up indefinitely.

Although patients on hormones seem to feel better, no one has been able to show that hormone therapy produces any consistent improvement in the bone structure or the demineralization the changes are usually permanent.

Another important aspect of the total treatment program is diet. While the patient is in the hospital, it is wise to discuss the dietary requirements and to insist on a general balanced diet with adequate amounts of protein. The diet should be supplemented by the aforementioned vitamins, minerals, and estrogens. Then, if the patient can be kept active, she seldom develops a recurrence of the back pain.

REFERENCES

1. NICHOLAS, J. A., AND OTHERS: Pathological fractures of the spine. *J. Bone Joint Surg., 42*-A:127-137, Jan. 1960.
2. LEWIN, PHILIP: *The Back and its Disk Syndromes,* 2nd ed. Philadelphia, Lea and Febiger, 1955.
3. SCULLY, F. J.: Choline salicylate: an effective well-tolerated drug for treatment of rheumatic diseases. *Southern Med. J., 53*:12-16, Jan. 1960.
4. NICHOLAS, J. A., AND WILSON, P. D.: Diagnosis and treatment of osteoporosis. *J.A.M.A., 171*:2279-2284, Dec. 26, 1959.

THE RESULTS OF EFFORTS FOR ASYMPTOMATIC DIAGNOSIS OF MALIGNANT DISEASE*

Victor A. Gilbertsen, M.D., and
Owen H. Wangensteen, M.D., F.A.C.S.,

T HE CANCER DETECTION CENTER program, a clinical investigative study, was initiated in 1948 with the presumption that earlier diagnosis of malignant disease would be followed by measurable improvement in therapeutic results. Objectives have included determination of the efficacy of current detection methods, estimation of the existence rates of presymptomatic cancers, evaluation of new or improved diagnostic innovations, and compilation of data related to the survival of patients found to have malignant disease.

Experience accumulated with progression of the study has also emphasized the value of the basic, elementary methods of examination of the patient. Concomitantly, the merit of incorporation of the teaching of such techniques in the medical education program has become increasingly evident, and currently students at both the undergraduate and postgraduate levels are participating in the educational activities of the Center. The applicability of the elementary diagnostic procedures is illustrated by the observation that most of the cancers found were detected by utilizing diagnostic techniques available to the medical profession for half a century or more.

Evaluation of apparent improvements in therapeutic results which might have occurred because of earlier diagnoses has necessitated the lapse of sufficient time to validate favorable early im-

*Surgery, Gynecology & Obstetrics, 116:413-416, April 1963.

pressions. In addition to current information pertaining to numbers of patients seen and examinations performed, survival data are presented herein. A sufficient number of cases and long enough follow-up period are available to provide reliable data on patients with primary cancers at various sites.

RESULTS

Since the inauguration of the Cancer Detection Center program in 1948, 10,771 patients have been examined, 5,139 men and 5,632 women. Examinations performed total 44,324, or an average of four examinations per patient.

Cancers detected since 1948 number 375. Thus, one cancer was found for each 110 examinations, or one for each twenty-nine participants. Of the cancers which have been detected, one-third were found at initial visits and two-thirds at follow-up examinations. Initial examinations revealed one cancer for each eighty-five patients; recheck examinations disclosed one cancer for each 135 patients.

Male patients had 200 of the 375 cancers found at the Center. The skin, as might be anticipated, was the most frequent site of involvement; fifty-five men had skin cancers. Next in frequency was the prostate gland; forty-five prostatic carcinomas were detected. Cancers of the skin, prostate gland, intestines, and stomach, in addition to leukemia, comprised more than 80 per cent of the cancers found in men.

In women, also, the skin was most commonly involved. The breast was the next most frequent site; thirty-eight breast cancers were found at the Detection Center. The skin, breast, intestines, uterus, and ovaries were the primary sites of 81 per cent of the cancers detected in women.

Breast. Twenty-five of the thirty-eight women with breast cancers were seen between 1948 and 1957, and, thus, five year follow-up studies are available. Six of the twenty-five patients had cancers which involved lymph nodes; one of the six died prior to treatment. The remaining five women underwent mastectomies performed for cure. Four of the five or 80 per cent were five year survivors. Nineteen of the twenty-five patients with breast cancers seen between 1948 and 1957 did not have any evidence of lymph node involvement. Each of the nineteen underwent a mastectomy performed for cure. Eighteen patients or 94.7 per cent were five year survivors.

Rectum. Twenty-nine patients had cancers of the rectum. Twenty-four of these patients were seen between 1948 and 1957; nineteen of the twenty-four or 79 per cent survived five years or more after operation. The twenty-four rectal cancers detected in the 1948 through 1956 period include carcinoid tumors. Each of the patients with a carcinoid was a five year survivor. The other twenty rectal cancers were adenocarcinomas; fourteen were found at initial examinations and six at follow-up examinations. Of the fourteen patients with carcinomas detected at initial examinations, nine or 64 per cent survived five years. Each of the six with a carcinoma which was found at follow-up examination has lived for a period of five years or longer.

Colon. Cancer of the colon was detected in thirty-one patients, eighteen of whom were seen between 1948 and 1957. Of the eighteen colon cancers, six were found at initial examinations; three of the six patients survived for five years. Follow-up examinations were responsible for detection of twelve colon cancers during the period; six of these twelve patients were five year survivors.

Stomach. Twenty-two patients examined at the Center had cancer of the stomach. Seventeen of the twenty-two were seen during the 1948 through 1956 period. One of the seventeen patients with gastric cancer had a carcinoid. She has now survived nine years without evidence of recurrence. The other sixteen patients with stomach cancers had adenocarcinomas. Three of the sixteen were five year survivors; one of the three, however, is known to have died of recurrent cancer five years and three months after operation and has not been tabulated as a "cure." Thus, of the sixteen patients with gastric carcinomas, two or 12.5 per cent survived for a period of five years without known recurrence.

Seven of the sixteen stomach carcinomas detected in the 1948 through 1956 period were found at initial examinations. Two of the seven patients lived for five years—including the five year three month survivor. Follow-up examinations revealed nine gastric carcinomas. One of the nine patients or 11 per cent was a five year survivor.

Known Cancers. Compilation was made of all cancers known to have existed in the 10,771 patients during the time of their participation in the Cancer Detection Center examination program. In addition to the 375 cancers detected at the Center, 123 others were diagnosed elsewhere during the period of participation, or within a period of one year thereafter.

Thus, the number of recognized cancers totaled 498, or an average of one for each 21.6 patients. As annual axaminations averaged four per patient, the rate of development of recognized cancer could be computed as one per 86.4 patients per year.

Cancer Detection Center examinations disclosed 75 per cent of the cancers identified among actively participating patients. Of the other 25 per cent of known cancers, a continuing patient awareness of signs and symptoms associated with likely malignant change often helped to foster a prompt diagnosis between examinations. Patients were urged to seek medical advice at once in the event of suspicious symptoms during the between-examination intervals. With breast cancers, for example, no patient who detected by self examination a subsequently proved malignant lesion waited until her annual follow-up Cancer Detection appointment before obtaining a medical examination and therapy.

It is also of interest that, as far as is known, all primary thyroid, lip, and rectal cancers which have developed in actively participating Cancer Detection patients have been found by examinations performed at the Center. On the contrary, our efforts to detect early asymptomatic cancers of the retina, pancreas, and gallbladder have failed.

DISCUSSION

During the past several decades malignant diseases have accounted for an increasingly substantial portion of officially reported deaths. Available mortality data appear to indicate a continuing trend in this direction. Studies aimed at discovery of the cause or cure of malignant diseases are currently being pursued in research centers throughout the world.

Even without discovery of a therapeutic panacea, however,

already available diagnostic methods appear potentially capable of obviating a substantial number of the presently occurring deaths. The data available from the Cancer Detection project permits an estimation of the potential improvement in therapeutic results achievable by earlier diagnosis of malignant disease.

The observations for the group of patients with breast cancer have been most encouraging in this regard. Nineteen of the twenty-five women or 76 per cent found to have breast cancers during the 1948 through 1956 period had no evidence of spread to lymph nodes, an indication of the relative promptness of diagnosis in this group of patients.

The five year survival rate of 88 per cent observed for the twenty-five women with breast cancers, when compared with the commonly reported over-all survival figure of 50 per cent, is also noteworthy. The 88 per cent survival rate appears to indicate a salvage of more that three-fourths of the 50 per cent of patients who might ordinarily be expected to die within five years after diagnosis has been made.

Patients with primary rectal cancers currently are considered to have an over-all five year survival rate of about 25 per cent. In the present study, fifteen or 75 per cent of the twenty patients who had rectal carcinomas detected in the 1948 through 1956 period were five year survivors. Thus, in the Detection Center group, two- thirds of the 75 per cent of usually anticipated failures achieved five years survival. Of especial note arc the survival data for the six patients with carcinomas which were found on follow-up examinations; each of the six patients has survived five years.

For patients with colon cancers, nine of the eighteen with lesions detected between 1948 and 1957 were five year survivors. When compared with the usual over-all survival rate of about 30 per cent, 29 per cent of anticipated survival failures appear to have been obviated in the group from the Cancer Detection Center.

The rate of five year survival, 24 per cent for seventeen patients, for patients with gastric cancers compares favorably with the reported over-all survival figure of 12.5 per cent. For the sixteen patients who had carcinomas of the stomach, however, the five year survival rate was 19 per cent, three of sixteen. If the patient who died of recurrence three months after expiration of the conventional five year follow-up period is excluded from the list of successful cases, then the rate of survival without known recurrence was 12.5 per cent, two of sixteen, a figure identical to that reported for symptomatic patients with cancers of the stomach.

Malignant diseases especially favorable for identification in a cancer detection clinic appear to include cancers of the rectum, lip, thyroid, and prostate gland, as well as leukemia. Both skin and breast cancers, in addition, permits self-examination methods to aid in prompt identification when manifestations appear during the between-examination intervals.

CONCLUSION AND SUMMARY

Early detection and prompt treatment of several varieties of cancer often appear to be followed by improvement in survival. Examples are cancers of the breast, rectum, colon, skin, and the cervix. Of particular note in the present study was the 100 per cent five year survival without recurrence for the group with rectal carcinomas detected at follow-up examinations.

Utilization of basic, well known techniques of examination continues to be of fundamental value in detecting early cancers. In the present study, the employment of techniques available to the medical profession for half a century or more was responsible for detection of most of the identified cancers. Identification of any substantial proportion of potentially curable cancers of the pancreas, gallbladder, and stomach appears to require methods other than those currently employed.

NUTRITIONAL PROBLEMS IN THE AGED*

M. K. Horwitt, Ph.D.

IF WE RECOGNIZE THAT THE growth processes are dependent upon the food we eat and assume that these growth processes within the body are counterbalanced by a destructive or aging process, then it is logical to consider nutrition to be one of the more important factors in the prolongation of health. In the past years, this logic has led many practicing nutritionists to reach for "better" nutrition for the old folk and this in turn was often interpreted so as to provide more food for the average older person. More recently, with wider recognition of the fact that nutritional requirements are more likely to decrease rather than to increase with age, the dietetic problem has become somewhat complicated by the need to include equivalent dietary essentials in a smaller caloric ration.

CALORIC REQUIREMENTS

The older person's lower need for calories is largely a result of the reduction of functional protoplasm and the progressive atrophy of muscle tissue. This decrease in active tissue has been indirectly recognized in tables used for the calculation of basal metabolic rate from oxygen consumption data. It is apparent from the reports of Shock[1,2] that a large part of the diminution in the activity of various organ systems in the aged may be due to a loss of active tissue. How much of this tissue loss is indirectly related to a progressive decrease in activity and how much to other factors remains to be determined, but the net result of this phase of the aging process is that less functioning tissue remains to be nourished.

*Geriatrics, 12:683-686, December 1957.

Is the need for fewer calories by the smaller mass of cytoplasm counterbalanced by a lower efficiency with which calories are utilized? Before the constituents of the diet can be of any benefit, the digestive processes must facilitate the subdivision and absorption of the nutrients ingested. This process is, in turn, followed by the distribution of the products of digestion to the intercellular matrix by the cardiovascular and lymphatic systems. There are suggestions that the older individual may have lower concentrations of digestive enzymes; furthermore, tolerance curves based upon the absorption of carbohydrates indicate that the products of digestion may remain in the blood of the aged for longer periods than in the younger individual.

It has been proposed that special digestive enzyme preparations might be used to supplement the digestive processes of the aged. In light of the fact that most tolerance curves performed on the aged show prolonged higher levels in the blood rather than lower levels,[3] one wonders what advantage is to be gained in attempting to increase further the elevated levels of lipid and carbohydrate observed after a meal. It appears that, if digestive efficiency has decreased, the extent of this decrease is less, proportionately, than the decrease in cardiovascular efficiency and of other functions which are involved in removal of products of digestion from the blood stream.

Extrapolating these observations, one may conclude that the products of digestion may tend to remain in the circulatory fluids longer in the old than in the young. However, there is little scientific evidence upon which to base a decision regarding the spacing of meals, although the need for decreasing lipid consumption appears to be indicated if only because the products of lipids tend to remain in the blood stream longer than other dietary components.[4] Support for the practice of keeping such meals low in fat is obtained from the work of Herzstein, Wang, and Adlersberg,[5] who showed that ingested lipids may remain in the blood stream at high levels for as long as twenty-four hours. Counter-acting the theoretic assumptions which follow from interpretation of blood clearance rates is the observation by experienced geriatricians that older persons are much more comfortable when meals are spread out over most of the day, in order to avoid hypoglycemia, which is so poorly tolerated by the aged.[6]

PROTEIN REQUIREMENTS

Although much has been written about the observation of protein deficiency in the aged, interpretations of this observation have led to some confusion. Difficulties in conducting long-term nutritional experiments have hindered progress in this field. One cannot deny that negative nitrogen balance has been observed in several short-term studies of older individuals, but there is no evidence to indicate that the old require more protein than the young. The basic problem is related to a lower consumption of protein by many old people as a consequence of economic, social, and dental inadequacies rather than to a need for more protein. Since excess protein is a most inefficient form of energy, one wonders how much harm may be done by recommending a larger allowance of protein for all older individuals. On the other hand, in planning the diet of the old, one must remember that in average circumstances, as their activity and caloric intake decrease, their protein consumption may also decrease. Therefore, an effort must be made to keep protein intake normal by planning a slightly higher concentration of protein foods in a lower caloric total. This can be accomplished by substituting protein for some of the fat which one prefers to eliminate from such diets.

There is no reason to doubt the adequacy of the National Research Council allowance of 65 gm. of protein per day. This requirement is based upon an estimation of 1 gm. of mixed protein per day for each kilogram of body weight of young individuals. This allotment probably allows for a factor of safety in the old in whom the proportion of the active tissue to total body weight is decreased. Any surplus protein thus provided may compensate for any existing decrease in the efficiency of protein utilization.

Experimentally, in past and current long-term Elgin Projects, 65 gm. of protein per day has always been adequate for both old and young subjects. Insofar as the excretion of amino acid in the urine may give a clue to amino acid requirements, it is interesting to note that after three years on a diet which provided 60 gm. of protein per day (half was meat) , old men excreted slightly greater amounts in the urine than did young men in an identical environment.[7] From these and other data reported,[3] it is probable that, within the usual limits of protein intake, there are increased amounts of amino acid in the urine of subjects on diets which provide extra protein. Such observations confirm the suggestion that the older men fare as well as younger men on a diet which provides 60 gm. of mixed protein per day. Furthermore, Kountz and associates have reported that it is difficult to keep older individuals on high levels of protein intake and that an increase of protein in such diets (to 1.5 gm. of protein per kilogram of body weight) leads to an increase in nonprotein nitrogen levels in the blood.[8]

CALCIUM REQUIREMENTS

One of the most important and perplexing problems in the nutrition of the aged is the question of calcium requirement. Some of the difficulties stem from inadequate knowledge about calcium requirements in general. This is complicated by the larger problem of osteoporosis in the aged. The loss of tissue protein with age seems to be associated with a simultaneous loss of calcium, for it seems to be as difficult for the older individual to retain extra calcium as to rebuild muscle tissue. One may speculate that both of these tendencies toward negative balance may be directly related to the progressive decrease in activity with age. On this basis, the increased retention of calcium may, like the retention of muscle protein, be related to the inhibition of muscle atrophy by increasing activity.[9] In other words, controlled programs of mild exercise may be as important in the prevention of negative calcium balance as they are in maintaining muscle tissue, irrespective of the nutritional intake. This is not to belittle the importance of adequate intake of calcium. Until better information is available, at least 0.8 mg. of calcium should be considered the daily allowance.[10]

FAT REQUIREMENTS

Presently, the problem of fat requirements in man is in a state of flux. It is controversial in almost every respect except for the general agreement that fats in the diet are not preferred by either the old patient or his advisors. Not only is there experimental evidence to prove that the aged have either a retarded up-take of fat or a slower clearing of fat in the blood stream,[5] but the frequent observation of chronic disease of the biliary tract or gallbladder further suggests that lipid transport may be sufficiently slowed in the aged to warrant a cautious attitude toward feeding them fat. Fat is the least desirable component of a low-calorie diet; the maintenance of a proper protein to calorie ratio in an inactive individual is difficult if much fat is ingested.

VITAMIN REQUIREMENTS

The vitamin requirements of the aged appear to be no different than those of the young.[3] Nevertheless, it is not surprising that more signs of vitamin inadequacy are found in the older group, and this may be especially true in those old people who are not institutionalized.[11] In view of the smaller caloric intake recommended and the lower chance, statistically, of having a correct mixture of the proper components in the diet, there may be greater justification for vitamin supplementation of the aged than of any other population group. Aside from the fact that a large percentage of older individuals may have some pathologic condition which requires specific treatment, the quest for food has become less of a satisfying experience for many of them. The reasons for this may be psychologic, economic, administrative, or dental but it exists in sufficient cases to make plausible the broad generalization that the restricted diet of many aged persons can be improved by moderate and sensible vitamin supplementation. The question of vitamin needs has been somewhat clouded by those who interpret an absence of frank clinical deficiency instead of optimum biochemical efficiency as a desirable goal. Supplementation with a part of the minimum daily vitamin requirement is often simpler to prescribe than doing a test for nutritional inadequacy and may prove a desirable form of nutritional anaphylaxis for old people.

No discussion of the nutritional needs of the aged is complete without mention of their need for adequate water. As many old people do not like water,[6] it may be necessary to suggest beverages or foods containing more water. Above two liters per day should be provided depending upon the weather and environment.

CONCLUSIONS

A real problem exists in maintaining the nutritional health of the older members of our population. Although a certain percentage of these people are overfed—and the undesirable consequences of overweight in the aged should always be kept in mind—enough of them are in a state of undernutrition with respect to proteins and some vitamins to warrant continued attention to their individual requirements. Discussions regarding the relative needs of the old and the young are not very helpful in judging the best course of action; the apparent increase in nutritional deficiencies among the elderly is not a result of altered requirement but is usually a sign of either individual, social, or dental neglect.

Although it is difficult to make generalizations that will cover all requirements, one might summarize by recommending: 1) a lowered basal caloric intake to match the decrease in active tissue mass and consequent lowered basal metabolic rate; 2) a decrease in fat intake, balanced by an increased concentration of protein in the diet in order to attain a level of consumption of about 1 gram of mixed protein per kilogram of body weight; 3) adequate fluid intake and sufficient bulk in the form of vegetables to counteract constipation; 4) minerals to supply accepted minimum needs with particular attention to calcium and iron; and 5) vitamins to meet minimum daily requirements, remembering that the somewhat altered composition of these diets favors a greater statistical incidence of nutritional deficiencies in the aged.

REFERENCES

1. SHOCK, N. W.: Metabolism and age. *J. Chronic Dis.*, 2:687, 1955.
2. SHOCK, N. W.: Some physiological aspects of aging in man. *Bull. N.Y. Acad. Med., 32*:268, 1956.
3. HORWITT, M. K., LIEBERT, E., KREISLER, O., AND WITTMAN, P.: Investigations of human requirements for B-complex vitamins. *National Research Council Bulletin,* No. 116, 1948.
4. BECKER, G.H., MEYER, J., AND NECHELES, H.: Fat absorption and atherosclerosis. *Science, 110*:529, 1949.
5. HERZSTEIN, J., WANG, CHUN-I, AND ADLERSBERG, D.: Fat-loading studies in relation to age. *Arch. Int. Med., 92*:265, 1953.

6. STIEGLITZ, E. J.: Nutrition problems of geriatric medicine. *J.A.M.A., 142:*1070, 1950.

7. HARVEY, C. C., AND HORWITT, M. K.: Excretion of essential amino acids by men on a controlled protein intake. *J. Biol. Chem., 178:*953, 1953.

8. KOUNTZ, W. B., ACKERMANN, P. G., KHEIM, T., AND TORO, G.: Effects of increased protein intake in older people. *Geriatrics, 8:*63, 1953.

9. BROZEK, J., AND KEYS, A.: Relative body weight, age, and fatness. *Geriatrics, 8:*70, 1953.

10. VINTHER-PAULSEN, N.: Calcium and phosphorus intake in senile osteoporosis. *Geriatrics, 8:*76, 1953.

11. PYKE, M., HARRISON, R., HOLMES, S., AND CHAMBERLAIN, K.: Nutritional value of diets eaten by old people in London. *Lancet, 253:*461, 1947.

INSOMNIA IN THE AGED*

Zachary Sagal, M.D.

Insomnia is defined as "prolonged inability to obtain due sleep, abnormal wakefulness" by Webster and as "inability to sleep in the absence of external impediments" by Stedman. Often the application of the term is purely subjective—the individual claiming to be suffering from insomnia while objectively he may be getting sufficient sleep.

One may call it pseudoinsomnia. Kleitman, in his classical monograph on *Sleep and Wakefulness*,[1] quotes Klingman as stating: "Those who sleep eight hours and believe that they need ten consider themselves to be suffering just as much of insomnia as others who cannot get more than four or five hours of sleep but who would be satisfied with six or seven." Thus, insomnia is largely an individual conception. Again quoting Kleitman: "Because of the variability in the depth and duration of sleep in different individuals, and in the same person from one season to another, there is no good objective criterion for calling a certain deviation from normal sleep pattern "insomnia." Not only does the duration and depth of sleep vary with the individual, but the observation of the so-called insomniac is often faulty."[2] In his splendid little booklet for the laity on "Insomnia," Alvarez says: "Nurses in hospitals commonly disagree with the patient who says: 'I didn't get a bit of sleep all night.' They say: 'He was asleep every time they looked in.' "[3]

WHAT IS THE NATURE OF SLEEP?

The literature on the nature of sleep is quite extensive. In 1939, in his widely quoted monograph, Kleitman listed 1,434

*Geriatrics, 13:463-466, July 1958.

179

references. Presumably there were many more that he didn't mention. A great deal of work has been reported since and important studies are being carried on right along, but it is the general consensus that knowledge of the nature of sleep is still sketchy. The physiologic effect of sleep on the various organs and their functions has been studied intensively, but the exact nature of sleep is not yet fully understood.

The ideas often propounded with reference to sleep and insomnia are quite amusing. A query sent in by a physician to the Journal of the American Medical Association was worded thus: "Has medical research found any means of eliminating waste products to allow patients with hardened head arteries to get more sleep?"[4] When it comes to lay people, even the best informed sometimes express bizarre notions. In a lecture on adult education delivered several years ago, a reprint of which is being widely distributed, Professor Mortimer Adler said, "Sleep is that part of life which is spent in recuperating from the fatigues of work. No one deserves to sleep who does not work. Sleep is for the sake of work." A similar thought is attributed to King Solomon, who said: "The sleep of a laboring man is sweet whether he eat little or much, but the abundance of the rich will not suffer him to sleep."[5]

To the layman, sleep is a definite and positive body function, glamorized in poem and song, greatly sought after and desired. The legitimate promotion of all sorts of appliances to aid in securing enough sleep has developed into a formidable industry. A furniture store in New York has for many years maintained a "Sleep Department" under the management of the whimsical Norman Dine. In an illustrated article in *Life* several years ago he exhibited an astounding number of items and gadgets used to induce restful sleep.

HOW MUCH SLEEP DO WE NEED?

The amount of sleep needed varies with individual requirements and is probably related to the hormonal, nervous, and temperamental make-up of the person. Adams, in Harrison's *Principles of Medicine* states that "the amount of sleep required by any one person is variable within rather narrow limits."[6] There is the old adage regarding the need for sleep: six hours for the man, seven for the woman and eight for the fool. Like many another saying this seems clever but has no basis in reality.

Few textbooks on physiology give definite figures as to the amount of sleep required at various ages. An exception is that by Best and Taylor which states: "The sleep requirements of different persons varies widely, it varies also with age . . . old persons require five to seven hours."[7] This estimate has been accepted by many gerontologists, but not universally. Most writers are satisfied with vague allusions to the progressive diminution of sleep requirements with advancing age and with the unwillingness of old people to accept the fact. In *Geriatric Medicine,* Stieglitz writes that "insomnia is common in the old."[8] He discusses causes, suggests remedies, but does not mention what he considers the normal duration of sleep. In an earlier publication he indicates that "our requirements for sleep change with aging," obviously implying that the older person needs less sleep.[9]

In reviewing the literature one gains the impression that there need not be any disagreement as to the sleep requirements, that it is generally known that infants sleep twenty to twenty-two hours out of twenty-four; children of preschool age, twelve to fourteen hours, and adolescents, eight to ten hours; and that as we grow older, we need less and less sleep. This was always my opinion, but I modified it recently under the impact of being brought in contact with a large group of older individuals.

Allusion is made to the fact that many brilliant men got along on very little sleep. Stieglitz writes: "There are those notable characters in history, such as Napoleon and Thomas Edison, who are reputed to have maintained their vigor and enthusiasm with an average of only four hours of sleep per night . . . However . . . [they] took frequent brief naps during. . . the day. In all probability their total period of somnolence was . . . six to six and a half hours."[9] Boas says that "most persons need less sleep as they grow older. . . Many. . . do well with six hours sleep. . . It is claimed that after the age of sixty-five many individuals sleep only four hours out of twenty-four, but this must be exceptional."[10] Then he modified it by saying: "Many as they grow older and feebler sleep as much as twelve hours a night."

Brown quotes Albutt as saying "Old people require more sleep than middle aged."[11] However, according to his own observation, "The older a man gets, the less sleep he appears to require ... He may *rest* many hours more—and usually does—but this should be distinguished from actual sleep." In a survey made of the sleep habits of 509 men of distinction, Laird gives as "maximum hours of sleep as related to age for age sixty-five—seven hours, forty minutes; seventy-five—seven hours, forty-five minutes; eighty-five— eight hours, ten minutes. Some young people had less than six hours while some old people had more than eight hours ... it has been generally believed that with increasing age there is less sleep, but the records of these 509 men have a slight tendency in the opposite direction."[12] In his summary he states that "there is a tendency with increased age to take more rather than less sleep." In a comparatively recent study of the subject, Ginsberg, a psychiatrist, says that "The most accepted concept among geriatricians is that elderly persons need less and less sleep than younger ones."[13] He quotes Jaspers who "goes so far as to say that the average duration of sleep falls to three or four hours after the age of sixty."[14] He also quotes Mueller: "Diminution of sleep is physiologic in advanced age."[15] Ginsberg himself did not find any significant statistical correlation between age and amount of sleep required. He lays great stress on the adaptational abilities of the old person.

THE RESTORATIVE EFFECT OF SLEEP

To add to the confusion regarding the required amount of sleep for the aged, there comes an Associated Press release from Moscow, under date of May 18, 1957. This release, reporting on the work of Professor Braines, stresses the value of large amounts of sleep as a factor in prolongation of life, even if the sleep is induced by artificial means. According to Professor Braines' theory, senility is caused by overstraining the main nerve processes in the cortex of the cerebrum but such damage can be repaired by much sleep.

The original article by Professor Braines, which appeared in the *Moscow Literary Gazette* in the May 18, 1957 issue, relates the case of a senile fifteen-year-old lap dog which, by means of artificially induced sleep treatments over a period of three months, was restored to good health. According to the description by Professor Braines, the dog, having nearly reached the age limit for its species, was in a state of extreme senile debility. She was apathetic, lying down most of the time; showed great muscular weakness and incoordination; had lost most of her teeth and fur, and was oblivious of anything about her.

The metamorphosis that took place after treatment was miraculous: the dog became active, muscletone and coordination improved, and fur grew in again. Now, six years later, at the age of twenty-one, the animal is active, reacts normally to environment, and still retains her sex instinct. The author does not state whether he means by this that she has normal estrus. Be that as it may, the results are remarkable. The rationale of this form of therapy, especially as it pertains to the postponement of the advent of senility, is based on the assumption that exhaustion of the vitality of the cerebral cortex accounts for the debility of old age.

Restoration of the normal processes of the cortical cells takes place during sleep. Before Pavlov's researches on the central nervous system, development of signs and symptoms of senility was considered to be caused by progressive hormonal deficiency, particularly that of the gonads. Pavlov and his school attach prime importance to the condition of the central nervous system. Professor Petrova, working in Pavlov's laborartory, was able to reverse the process of developing, artificially-induced senility in young animals by treating the cortex of the cerebral hemispheres.

As a continuation of these experiments, Professor Braines induced premature senility in young rats and monkeys by exhaustion of the cortical cells, and then rejuvenated them by induction of artificial sleep. Braines believes that the insomnia which is common with advancing age is a potent factor in causing senility by failure to allow sufficient time for the restorative processes to take effect. By prolonging the periods of sleep a favorable balance in the metabolism of the nervous system can be brought about, thus conserving the life potency of the individual and forestalling development of senility.

Even if we do not accept this theory in its entirety, it makes us wonder whether a revision of our notions with relation to sleep are not due for a thorough revision. Possibly the aging person's craving for more sleep and the complaints of insomnia, justified or otherwise, are manifestations of an instinctive urge for a chance to counteract the inroads of the degenerative processes. The tendency of old people to doze off and to take frequent naps may not be due so much to their state of debility as to the need for extra periods of somnolence to replenish spent nervous energy and to restore the cortical cells to their normal state.

The prevailing notion that the older one gets the less sleep he needs may be incorrect and the opposite may be true—with advancing age, the older person needs more sleep as the basis for good health and as a prophylactic against premature aging. The very concept of "normal" and of "premature" aging perhaps needs revision. Professor Braines reminds us of the theoretic researches of Metchnicoff, Bogomoletz, and Lasareff, which led them to believe that a life span of 150 years can be eventually hoped for.

WHAT CAN BE DONE FOR INSOMNIA?

It has been my opinion for many years that with advancing years less and less sleep is required for maintenance of normal health. I had many arguments with patients and friends to convince those who were not satisfied with five or six hours of sleep. The advice to just rest in bed if unable to sleep was rarely taken kindly.

Lately I have come to agree with Dr. Alvarez, who, on many occasions, has advocated the use of mild soporifics, for he is convinced of the innocuousness of their use over long periods. A colleague and classmate of mine has been taking routinely 3 gr. of Seconal every night for many years without any ill effect, not even a morning hangover. On several occasions, his wife told me how she would often lie awake at night and envy his deep sleep. She tried taking a small dose of barbiturate, but it made her drowsy all day following. One must remember that there is an individual sensitivity to soporifics and that people react differently to them. Lately, I have come to the conclusion that there is no hard and fast rule to go by and each case must be treated individually.

REFERENCES

1. KLEITMAN, N.: *Sleep and Wakefulness*. Univ. of Chicago Press, 1939, p. 379.
2. *Ibid.,* p. 380.
3. ALVAREZ, W. C.: *Insomnia*. New York: Harper & Bros., 1942.
4. Queries and Therapeutic Notes. *J.A.M.A., 161*:174, 1957.
5. *Ecclesiastes, 5*:12.
6. HARRISON, T. R.: *Principles of Medicine*. The Blaskiston Co., 1954.
7. BEST, C. H., AND TAYLOR, N. B.: *The Physiological Basis of Medical Practice,* 5th Ed. The Williams & Wilkins Co., 1950, p. 1051.
8. STIEGLITZ, E. J.: *Geriatric Medicine,* 3rd Ed., J. P. Lippincott Co., 1954, p. 129.
9. STEIGLITZ, E. J.: *The Second Forty Years*. J. P. Lippincott Co., 1946, p. 68.
10. BOAS, E. P.: *Treatment of the Patient Past Fifty,* 3rd. Ed., The Year Book Publishers, 1947, p. 55.
11. BROWN H.: *Sleep and Sleeplessness*. Hutchinson & Co., London, 1910, p. 35.
12. LAIRD, D. A.: A Survey of the Sleep Habits of 509 Men of Distinction (Art, Literature, Science, etc.). *Am. Med., 37*:271, May 1931.
13. GINSBERG, R.: Sleep and sleep disturbance in geriatric psychiatry. *J. Amer. Geriatrics Soc., 3*:493-511, 1955.
14. JASPERS, K. (quoted by Ginsberg: *Allgemeine Psychopathologie*. Berlin, 1946, p. 196.
15. MUELLER, L. R. (quoted by Ginsberg). *Ueber den Schlaf*. Berlin, 1948, p. 149.

SENIOR CITIZEN AT THE CROSSROADS*

REHABILITATION

How much hope and how much help is offered the ailing senior citizen? Is attention paid to his most common complaints—the hearing and vision that are not what they once were; his loss of teeth and difficulty in chewing; his impaired bowel function, or his painful feet?

Dr. Frank W. Reynolds[2] calls attention to the importance of the little things, and the dangers of passing off valid complaints as being due to old age. He sees the aging individual taking his first step toward social isolation if this farsightedness remains uncompensated, or the cataract and glaucoma are untreated. He becomes discouraged if he tries to read or do close work; this invites limitations in the very activities which become more important in maintaining social relationships in the later years. The hearing loss which discourages conversation encourages withdrawal from others.

"After the age sixty-five," says Reynolds, "the average person has only eight of his original thirty-two teeth." Toothlessness not only leads to poor eating patterns which undermine health; the personal appearance deteriorates at the time of life when it becomes important to preserve it. Health counseling may prevent sometimes harmful dependence on artificial catharsis; and the cause of discomfort from constipation should be investigated by a physician. Care of painful feet and properly fitted shoes may enable some elderly bed or wheel-chair patients to return to a degree of independence and activity, and may prevent dependence in some others.

---

*What's New, 216:4-10, 1960, Courtesy of Abott Laboratories.

Unfortunately, properly fitted and comfortable dental plates, eyeglasses, hearing aids or shoes are apt to be fairly expensive, and may be beyond the means of an aged individual. They are also among the most common exclusions to benefits in health insurance programs.

In his program for health counseling, Reynolds[2] stresses the special need of the aged for a periodic health examination. He reminds us of the chronic nature and insidious onset of most of their ills. Usually such ills as heart or cerebrovascular disease, cancer, or osteoporosis can be diagnosed by the physician before they become manifest to the patient. As the human body loses some of its capacity to react to disease with aging, and old people generally have comparatively high thresholds to pain, he warns, "One may see acute appendicitis or advanced pulmonary tuberculosis in an older person who does not appear to be acutely ill and who may have only mild discomfort." His observation would seem to be well substantiated by a recently reported study of death certificates in the state of California.[3] A surprising number of deaths which were due primarily to tuberculosis had no records of morbidity from this disease. These deaths from previously unreported tuberculosis occurred largely among the aged.

Would diagnostic service benefits in insurance programs increase costs to such a degree that the price of premiums would be beyond the means of not only the aging but all average individuals? A Blue Shield program in Maryland[4] offered employees in one heavy industry and their dependents up to $75 each in any one year for diagnostic services in or out of a hospital. Over a two-year period, hospitalization was increased. On the other hand, Dr. Russell S. Ferguson[5] found a striking decrease in hospitalization among OAS recipients in Santa Cruz county, California, who received diagnostic examinations and care for uncovered health defects. Only seventeen of 664 were in nursing or boarding homes in a forty-two-month follow-up period. Total time of their institutionalization was 174.5 months; total cost, $19,966. In contrast, 200 of the average OAS roll of 3416 are continuously in institutions as a minimum cost of no less than $25,000 every month.

Whatever the cost of diagnostic services and care of uncovered defects may be, neglect of the defects invites the higher cost of rehabilitation or long-term care. Too many physicians are confronted with the problem of salvaging what is left of the neglected health of their aged patients. Dr. Howard A. Rusk[6] has said that rehabilitation is medicine's number-one problem. And the number-one problem of the physician who has a patient in need of rehabilitation is the lack in his own community of a particular facility or service he requires for the proper placement of his patient.

Just how do citizens in a community become interested in providing an adequate health program for themselves? This was the problem facing Dr. Harold D. Chope[7] in 1948 as director of San Mateo county department of health and welfare in California. The almost overwhelming influx of new residents into this area had begun; and in the preceding years World War II had prevented even the normal increase in their public health facilities, recruitment of new leaders in some disciplines, and in reorganization.

But by the beginning of 1958 Dr. Chope was able to say, "A forgotten part of this county has been found; what to many was a life without hope has become a life with purpose and dignity. Not just a few disinherited individuals have been provided for; the entire county has become involved in the problems and satisfactions of rehabilitation.

"There was a new 120-bed tuberculosis hospital, an enlarged county hospital, and the health and welfare divisions had moved from the basement in the county court house to an administration building on the hospital site. There was considerable fomentation regarding rehabilitation, much of it coming from Dr. Lester Breslow, chief of the bureau of chronic diseases of the California state department of health.

"The desire for a rehabilitation program existed with administrative medical personnel; and various specialties in medicine made major contributions. But I think it is only fair to point out that the real leadership came from the social work discipline.

"Until February, 1954, the Crystal Springs Home in San Mateo county had been operated as a 'relief home' with the 'inmates' receiving 'custodial care for elderly indigents.' Then the superintendent of the social services division recommended a new manager, Einor Nordby. He brought to our problem good training, broad experience, and other characteristics of inestimable value. He had a strong conviction about the values of rehabilitation, an abiding faith in the infinite capacity of human beings to overcome seemingly insuperable handicaps; and he had a sincere respect for human dignity.

"Within a few weeks the 'relief home' had become the Crystal Springs Rehabilitation Center; 'inmates' had become patients; and 'custodial care for elderly indigents' became 'rehabilitation services for patients with long-term illness.' It didn't take long to change names and terms. It did take Einor Nordby a little longer to develop the program and philosophy, and to teach a largely untrained staff to center their efforts on restoring dignity, status, self-respect and self-esteem in the individual patient.

"The nutrition department of the state health department surveyed the dietary and it was promptly improved. Little things were done to indicate to the patients that the management considered them human beings capable of personal decisions, and with opinions of value in determining policy.

"Mealtimes were arranged to suit the patients instead of the staff. Food was served as attractively as possible instead of prison-style. Patients were consulted on their likes and dislikes; sugar and condiments were placed on the table to afford them a free choice in seasoning their food. And they were offered a before-bedtime snack of graham crackers and milk.

"A second form of motivation was provided through committees on activities, arts and crafts, the library and patients' services, all to discuss policy and program. Because of budgetary limitations, Mr. Nordby and his committees turned to the community for volunteer help.

"The relief home had been shunned by the community, except for those who 'wanted to do something for the poor' during the holiday season. Now there was a new spirit that was hard to describe, but immediately felt. Community organizations became enthusiastic sponsors of various rehabilitation activities; they provided tools, money, qualified teachers and other workers.

"These activities gave status and helped restore sadly depleted self-esteem in the patients. 'Inmates' were again human beings with personalities and skills. There was new hope and incentive; but this was not enough. The physically disabled were still disabled though their outlook was improved. The mildly depressed responded well, but the severely depressed were still depressed. A psychiatrist, physical therapist, occupational therapist and social service worker gave their part-time voluntary services.

"Within the next two years the demonstrated accomplishments convinced the county board of supervisors. We started in 1958 with a psychiatrist, physiatrist, two internists, a vocational counselor, all of them part-time; a full-time nursing director with her master's degree and experience in care of the chronically ill, a psychiatric social worker, and dietitian. The patient who enters Crystal Springs from our county hospital has the benefit of continuing therapy. His records accompany him, and all disciplines on both staffs cooperate closely in the achievement of his rehabilitation.

"What does such a type of service for a 135-bed rehabilitation center cost the county's taxpayers? In 1953-54 indigent custodial care cost $4.96 per patient-day; the annual increase was to $5.50, $6.00, and to $7.55 per patient-day in 1956-57—a 52 per cent increase in cost. But this is not all chargeable to rehabilitation. Professional staff salaries, supplies and equipment associated with rehabilitation amount to 45 cents per patient-day."

At Crystal Springs patients have made many of the things they need and adapted others that were there. They raise money by selling beautiful hand-crafted articles they produce, and buy materials or equipment.

"What does the county taxpayer get for his money? During 1956-57 there were twelve patients restored to full-time employment, completely relieving the taxpayers of an annual cost of $2756 for each of them; this represents a total saving of $33,072. About 250 patients had returned to varying levels of employment or independent living within the five-year period ending early in 1959."

But to Dr. Chope and Mr. Nordby these are not the important results. "What criteria do we have," asks Dr. Chope, "to measure the worth of human dignity to the individual? What is it worth to the family of a man who contemplated suicide because he was totally defeated? What is the money value of one or ten years of active, independent and productive living to a man who is so rejected and disabled at fifty-five that he feels discarded by society? Can society afford to rescue a woman of seventy from the living death of permanent bedrest with its attendant evils of premature senility and retrogression to infantilism?

"We are much happier to be responsible for an institution around which the community rallies—with the garden club planning landscape projects, the cosmetologist association helping to start a beauty parlor, and church groups providing spiritual counseling—than to be responsible for the operation of a 'poorhouse.'

"The tangible rewards of expanded institutional care still left much to be done for those outside institutions. A study of General Assistance recipients showed that 58 per cent of them were dependents because of alleged poor health. This might seem to be a serious indictment of a health department which has the modern facilities for prevention and treatment of physical illness. In February, 1955, we employed an internist to give thorough physical examinations to these recipients.

"A review of the findings showed that 75 per cent of the men fell into five diagnostic categories: chronic alcoholism, chronic pulmonary disease, hypertensive vascular disease, neurological disease and orthopedic defects. The women presented a different picture: 40 per cent had a diagnosis of psychoneurosis or psychosis; 23 per cent had no diagnosable disease.

"In September, 1955, we began testing recipients for potential rehabilitation according to five factors: motivation, physical condition, skills and abilities, personal adjustments including intelligence, and social adjustment. We found that 50 per cent of them had a sufficiently high rating to justify further efforts on our part.

"Later we found that some of these had suffered such a long series of tragic experiences and endured them for such a prolonged time that they had come to passive acceptance of their dependency and disability roles. Many had lost all courage to find or hold a job because they had been rebuffed so many times.

"In 1956 we started a work experience program. We made the effort to place recipients in county departments where their skills fitted the jobs. Mechanics were put to work on the county cars;

women with sewing skills were placed in sewing rooms in the institutions; and we found clerical jobs for those whose abilities indicated them. This relatively sheltered work experience was sufficient in a surprising number of cases to convince a recipient that he was able to work; many sought and obtained private employment. In 1957, we established an industrial rehabilitation workshop under a trained occupational therapist.

"A health officer doesn't need an organization such as ours to further rehabilitation. One in a nearby county has done an outstanding job with the traditional organization. If we are to pursue vigorously the now accepted objective of reducing chronic disease and improving mental health, those on our welfare rolls offer us a rich field to develop techniques and administrative study."[7]

There are other outstanding rehabilitation facilities and services in this state, but in 1958 the California state department of health reported the most urgent need on a statewide basis was for comprehensive rehabilitation facilities with inpatient and outpatient services for the severely disabled; and for facilities where personnel can be trained to organize and operate rehabilitation services in hospitals and in the other facilities which are available to patients during the early stages of their disabilities.[8]

The California plan for meeting their rehabilitation and long-term care needs has implications for other communities now seeking answers to these problems. One comprehensive rehabilitation center is planned for each of the five major geographical areas in the state; these will be supplemented by additional facilities in each of these areas for care of limited disabilities and age groups. It is estimated that three beds are needed for long-term care in chronic-disease hospitals and nursing homes for every thousand residents. Chronic disease hospitals will be required to maintain complete rehabilitation facilities of the chronically ill patient. In general the view is held that chronic disease facilities should be closely integrated with general hospital programs, and that nursing homes should be affiliated with the general hospital as a related institution providing limited services for the long-term care.

In 1958, there was a substantial change in the licensing law for California nursing homes. They are now *required* to conduct social and recreational activity programs for their patients and to encourage their participation in these programs.[9-10] This require-ment aims at ambulation, self-help and rehabilitation in the nurs-ing home patients, and provision of space for ambulant patients.

As Gordon R. Cumming[10] has pointed out, "There is new emphasis on the need for the nursing home or other institution which cares for the aged to develop a competence to provide for the patient as his condition changes, and assure him security and continuity of care. This emphasizes the importance of some type of affiliation between nursing homes and hospitals."

Evidence is growing in support of the observation of Dr. Robert Felix[6] that "Relatively little has been done to develop medical rehabilitation services for the aged, largely because of the pessimistic attitude among physicians, families, and the aged them-selves." The taxpayer will demand suitable rehabilitation and liv-ing facilities for the aged in his community, if he is ever made aware of the enormous financial burden he creates for himself when he permits an ailing senior citizen to be improperly placed or kept in custodial care at a time when he has some potential for rehabilitation—just because he has no other place to go.

The average Illinois taxpayer probably does not know that his annual bill for nursing home care of the dependent aged in his state amounts to millions of dollars and is still rising, even though the number of aged on Old Age Assistance (OAA) rolls is declining. Partly because of OAST payments, all but 6 per cent of Illinois residents between the ages of sixty-five and seventy are able to care for themselves financially. It is quite different when they reach the ages between seventy-five and eighty; then about two thirds are OAA recipients; and about 12,000 of the some 25,000 nursing home patients in Illinois are on the OAA roll.[12] According to a 1953-54 survey made by the Public Health Service and Commission on Chronic Illness,[11] the average patient remains in a nursing home for one year, and nearly a fifth of them three or more years.

The taxpayers' bill for the Illinois Medical Care program for the single month of July, 1959, was $3,134,304, and $2,154,433 of this was for OAA recipients: $1,050,288 for those in nursing homes; $601,061 for those in hospitals; and $503,084 for other medical care expenses. This is an average monthly bill.[12] It does not take complex calculations to see the ominous problem that such bills present for taxpayers in the future. It is estimated that there will be 21 million individuals in the United States by 1975 who are sixty-five years of age or older; this will be about six million more at this age than there are today. If our high birth rate continues, there will be fewer working people in proportion to support even bigger numbers of both the very young and very old.

There was a 75 per cent jump in cost of nursing home care for Illinois OAA recipients between 1951 and 1953. This led the Advisory Committee on Aging[12] of the Illinois Public Aid Commission, under the chairmanship of William L. Rutherford, to propose a rehabilitation research and education program to see how much the numbers of OAA recipients who were entering nursing homes and state mental hospitals might be reduced. As a result, three demonstration programs were started in Illinois in 1956-57.

At Peoria a Rehabilitation Education Service (RES)[13] was started in February, 1957, to provide the staffs of nursing homes in Illinois with techniques and materials needed to carry out medically prescribed rehabilitative care of their patients. This service is a joint project of the United States Office of Vocational Rehabilitation, Illinois Public Aid Commission, and the Peoria Forest Park Foundation. (This not-for-profit, nonsectarian organization has supported various programs for the handicapped, including the Peoria Institute of Physical Medicine and Rehabilitation with divisions in three Peoria hospitals.) RES has been in thirty-seven nursing homes in over twenty-two counties; these homes care for over 2000 patients. However, no patient can be included in the program or receive any rehabilitation therapy without a prescription from his physician.

Dr. H. Worley Kendall of the Peoria Institute provides the medical supervision for RES and the two teams of highly skilled rehabilitation-nursing and occupational-therapy consultants who are employed by the commission with approval of the institute. Dr. Kendall conducts staff meetings in each nursing home at the beginning and end of the teaching program. These are attended by the nursing home staff and members of the RES team. The RES team works in the home four days a week for a period which varies from five to seven weeks. Mondays are reserved for follow-up visits in home previously visited. An annual evaluation of the RES program takes place in each home, with intensive training of the staff if any weakness has developed in the staff procedures. John A. Hackley, division of services for aging and rehabilitation, Illinois Public Aid Commission, is supervisor of the RES program.

The staff of the convalescent home of LaSalle county at Ottawa[14] is one of those which takes justifiable pride in the improvements achieved in their patients. In 1957, this home was established on the vacant floor of the Highland tuberculosis sanitarium at the suggestion of the county medical society. It has thirty-three beds for the care of the chronically ill and aged. "When the patients were admitted," says Dr. H. V. Madsen, "we found they were badly in need of general care and rehabilitation." The nursing home superintendent requested RES.

The patients looks forward to rehabilitation sessions; nurses took in added interest in the patients; and the patients found a renewed interest in life. Rehabilitative care has done wonders for some, and most of them are deeply grateful for improvement in their conditions. The philosophy or rehabilitation changes the climate in a nursing home; patients are amazingly cheerful in this home despite loss of eyesight, confinement to a wheelchair, or other serious handicaps. Though their average age is between seventy-five and eighty years, twenty-eight of the ninety patients treated here during the first year were discharged in improved condition.

As a result of the three-year RES research-study program, the commission has approved a continuation and expansion of this service.[12] The U.S. Office of Vocational Rehabilitation has offered assistance to other states interested in developing this type of program in nursing homes, and the state of Washington has started a similar demonstration program in its nursing homes.

Those responsible for the Illinois RES program stress the limitations of such a service and those conditions necessary to secure its maximal effects. In the first place, this service does not make a nursing home a substitute for a hospital or a rehabilitation center. If a patient requires the services of these facilities, his physician should consider his transfer to the appropriate facility. The nursing home can be an important facility in maintaining gains made by the patient in a hospital or rehabilitation center. But a lack of qualified, trained nurses can limit the rehabilitative services the nursing home can offer; and a rehabilitative nursing and activities program cannot be expected to succeed as a permanent addition to the nursing home program, if the staff lacks necessary training in patient care, or is without the basic knowledge of handling the daily needs of the sick.

If RES is not integrated into the total plan of medical care for the patient it cannot have its maximal effect. No program designed to provide dynamic progress patient care can succeed in a lasting way without continued support and direction of organized medicine in its established leadership role. When a nursing home is the only medical facility available, the physician has a real responsibility to aid the administrator in developing and maintaining the services required by his patient.

Moreover, RES cannot solve such problems as: improper placement of patients in facilities; a conflict between nursing home standards and a low rate of pay for their services; lack of medical interest in the chronically ill or aged; or any other community deficiency that may affect the patient's course, such as a lack of suitable homes for rehabilitated patients, home care programs, counseling or case worker services.

Experience with RES has frequently produced evidence that general hospital staffs should concern themselves more with better preventive rehabilitative care for their patients, which could prevent development of those problem-conditions that often unnecessarily create the need for nursing home care following hospitalization for acute illness. This observation strongly supports a similar one made by the Council on Chronic Illness.[13]

In 1956, hospital beds were provided in the Peoria Institute, and in Michael Reese and Resthaven Rehabilitation hospitals at Chicago, for a demonstration Geriatrics Rehabilitation Program (GRP) to determine how much rehabilitation of the ailing aged might reduce their admissions to nursing homes and state mental hospitals. A director of GRP was appointed to serve in each county. By June 30, 1958, ninety-four patients whose average age was over seventy-five years had been returned from nursing homes to the community; forty-nine had been rehabilitated in Cook county at Chicago; and forty-five at Peoria.

Results of the GRP in Chicago up to March 31, 1959, have been reported by Dr. Edward E. Gordon,[15] chairman of the department of physical medicine at Michael Reese hospital. Over a two-year period 149 nursing home patients were referred to GRP in Cook county. A physician and social service worker made an evaluation of rehabilitation potential in these patients at the nursing homes; as a result, 118 cases were given to the admissions committee for consideration. This committee is composed of Dr. Gordon and his staff at Michael Reese, related personnel, the medical director of Resthaven hospital, and the county GRP director.

Of the 118 patients considered by the committee, forty-two were rejected largely because of irremedial hip fracture or cerebrovascular disease to a degree that precluded treatment. The median age of the seventy-six patients admitted to the GRP was seventy-six years, and they presented 190 diagnoses. In forty-three, hemiplegia and hip fracture far exceeded all other motor disorders primarily underlying disability. Primary nonmotor disorders in the thirty-three others were due largely to cardiac and respiratory impairment. Measured improvement was achieved in 92 per cent of those with motor disabilities; thirty-three were able to return to the community. Similar improvement occurred in 95 per cent of the thirty-three with nonmotor disabilities; and twenty-eight were able to give up residence in a nursing home.

These sixty-one patients have received continuous follow-up though the outpatient geriatric clinic at Michael Reese and their gains have been maintained for a average of ten months. At the time of this report the difference between the cost of 637 patient-months of community living and that for nursing home care had saved the taxpayers $31,200. The cost of rehabilitation was met primarily by the Illinois Public Aid Commission, assisted by the United States Public Health Service.

Failure of rehabilitation in fifteen patients made it necessary to return them to nursing home care. Experience showed that psychiatric examination of sensorial function should become an in-

tegral part of initial evaluation for rehabilitation potential in the
aged.

As most of the patients responded readily to motor retraining,
superficial psychological support, and definitive medical treatment, it was concluded that planned *comprehensive* care of the
aged, including early rehabilitative services, in a general hospital
may well circumvent much of the expense and morbidity entailed
in routine nursing home placement if adequate home finding services are available. As the main primary disabilities often could
be favorably affected by drugs and restorative training, this success
suggests that both hospital and general practice are lagging behind
the forefront of medical and sociological therapeutics in care of
the aged.

However, without close and continuous support extended by
the social service worker, attitudes and initiative of the patients on
admission often might have militated against a successful outcome.[15]

Dr. Maurice E. Linden[16] believes that mental health is the
most neglected aspect of the health problems of the aged. In his
opinion the most important message for the physician is the promise of response to therapy found among elderly people. He finds
that when expectations are on a realistic basis the percentage of
recovery from mental illness is about the same for the aged as it
is for any other age: about one third can be helped a great deal;
another third moderately so; and the other third not at all. He calls
attention to important programs developing in care of the aged in
VA hospitals.

Probably a shortage of trained personnel presents the most
serious delay to progress. In California the Short-Doyle Act of
Community Mental Health Services, patterned on legislation
passed in New York state in 1954, was effective in September,
1957. It provides state payments on a 50-50 matching basis to
cities or counties for local services in treating the mentally ill. The
services are available to voluntary patients who are unable to obtain private psychiatric care, whether for financial, geographical
or other reasons. The patient is charged for services according to
his ability to pay.

By May, 1959,[17] there were forty-two services established in twelve counties throughout the state. But as soon as a local service is organized it is overwhelmed with demands for assistance. Every clinic has been swamped with referrals, and as more communities establish these services the shortage in personnel becomes even more acute.

Any attempt to make a comprehensive report of present developments of facilities and services for the aging would be out of date before it was published. Old facilities are adopting new methods and philosophies that better meet the needs of the aged; at the same time many new facilities are in construction. Notwithstanding, Eliot Richardson[18] warns, "Too few communities have adequate facilities for long-term care of the chronically-ill and dependent elderly person ... this has become the political problem of great moment. *It will not go away.* The real issues center around the degree of public action needed. Some would say that far more federal action is needed; others insist that Uncle Sam is already in too deep. But activities of local jurisdictions in working out solutions to health problems of the aged are spotty, sporadic and for the most part inadequate."

The situation has much in common with the chaotic conditions that prevailed during war. During World War II the federal government surveyed the entire country to mobilize our capacity for production of goods. They "knew" where every piece of machinery was. At that time an Ohio manufacturer called in a labor relations counselor because a union requested an election for his employees, and the manufacturer told them he was forced to shut down the plant because he couldn't find the kind of lathes needed to produce his contract. The counselor went across the street where a plant was already shut down to see if a vacant room could be used to hold the union election. He was curious to know why they were shut down. He was told that they couldn't get a contract for the lathes they had—the very kind of lathes needed by his client across the street! The next day both plants were back in production. Answers to community problems are apt to be lost when solutions are attempted somewhere away from the community.

In this series of four articles on the socioeconomic-health problems of the senior citizen we have presented a few selected, successful approaches or solutions, in the hope that they may prove helpful to those seeking answers to problems of the aging in their own communities. Some analysis of their success will reveal certain features which they have in common. In each community there were foresighted, able citizens who were capable of achieving adequate solutions with those ways and means which were at hand. It took time, frequently a few years—time to educate the citizens in their communities to recognize the needs of their aged; and it took leadership with unremitting work to secure the community support necessary to establish and maintain their services and facilities for their senior citizens.

The average American hears constantly of the problems of the aged, and little about such solutions in communities other than his own. A little more knowledge might prevent him from pushing the panic button which would further reduce the buying power of all citizens through more taxes and inflation—and most of all the buying power of the fixed, tax-ridden income of the senior citizen.

The real need for the aged is the same as it has always been. It is heard in the ancient plea of King David the psalmist: "Cast me not off in the time of old age; forsake me not when my strength-faileth."[19] The answer for today is voiced by a farsighted twentieth-century physician[5]: "To do so is extravagant waste." We cannot afford to neglect the needs of the senior citizen. Neglect is too costly and the losses accrue to us all. The more we scrutinize the accumulating facilities and services which adequately meet the needs of the aging, the more we find "The basic responsibility for meeting the problems of aging lies with the citizens in each community."[1]

REFERENCES

1. KUPLAN, L.: *Geriatrics, 13*:808-814, December 1958, and personal communications.
2. REYNOLDS, F. W., M.D.: Health counseling for individuals and groups. *New York State J. Med., 59*:833-842, March 1, 1959.
3. BOGEN, E., M.D., AND KUPKA, E., M.D.: *Dis. of the Chest, 35:* 597-606, June 1959.

4. Latros, Outpatient Care—No Bargain. *Medical News* Sept. 30, 1959.
5. Senior citizen at the crossroads. *What's New, 215:*10-16, 1959.
6. LYNCH, J. P., M.D.: Clinical and community implications of chronic illness in the aging process. *Virginia Medical Monthly, 86:*498-504, Sept., 1959.
7. CHOPE, H. D., M.D.: *Public Health Reports, California, 73:*42-46, January 1958; Rehabilitation in San Mateo; Public Health and Public Medical Care, *California Med., 85:*220-225, October, 1956; Personal communications with Einor Nordby and investigation of Crystal Springs Home.
8. Hospitals for California, 1958 Progress Report, State of California Dept. of Health, Berkeley.
9. Hospital Licensing Act and Requirements (effective date, July 30, 1958), page 30, State of California Dept. of Health, Berkeley.
10. CUMMING, G. R.: chief, Bureau of Hospitals, California State Dept. of Health, Berkeley: Nursing Homes Standards and Services, Past, Present and Future, at American Nursing Homes Association convention, San Francisco, September 9, 1958.
11. BROWN, F. R.: *Social Security Bulletin,* May 1958, U.S. Dept. H.E.W., Nursing Homes: Public and Private Financing of Care Today.
12. BRECKINRIDGE, MRS. ELIZABETH: Supervision, Section on Services for Aging and Rehabilitation, division of Field Operations, Illinois Public Aid Commission, Chicago; valuable assistance and loan of reports on GRP and RES.
13. HACKLEY, J. A.: coordinator, RES, Illinois Public Aid Commission at Peoria; condensation of his RES report at Rocky Mountain Conference on Aging, AMA, May 9, 1959; personal investigation of RES at Peoria, Ottawa and Dixon, Ill. Personal communications with: H. Worley Kendall, M.D., William L. Rutherford, chairman of the advisory committee on aging, Illinois Public Aid Commission and administrative vice-president, Forest ark Foundation, Peoria, Illinois. Illinois.
14. Personal investigation, Highland Sanatorium and Convalescent Home of LaSalle county, Ottawa, Ill.: H. V. Madsen, medical director, and A. Mambourg, R.N., superintendent.

15. Personal communication: E. E. Gordon, M.D., chairman department of physical medicine, Michael Reese hospital, Chicago; his two-year report of evaluation and rehabilitation of indigent geriatric subjects, August 17, 1959.

16. LINDEN, M. E., M.D.: Rehabilitation of the mentally ill aged. *Mental Hospitals, 10:*7-10, October 1959; personal communications.

17. AUERBACK, A., M.D.: The Short-Doyle Act for Community Mental Health Services, State of California Dept. of Mental Hygiene. *California Med., 90:*335-338, May, 1959; *The Short-Doyle Act,* second edition, August 1958.

18. Health Needs of the Aged Take on Political Importance (editorial,). *J. Iowa Med. Society, 48:*686, December 1958, quoting assistant secretary of U.S. Dept. H.E.W., Eliot Richardson.

19. *Psalm, 71:9.*

PSYCHOLOGICAL ASPECTS OF AGING*

Francis J. Braceland, M.D.

COMMENTS UPON VARIOUS aspects of old age and aging abound in the writings of the sages and the dramatists down through the years, but interest in the underlying psychology, the psychopathology, and the mental hygiene of aging is of relatively recent vintage. The brushes of the ancient observers painted broadly, if not brightly, and in the times of Terence, Cicero and Sanctorius old age was frequently regarded as a disease. Cicero wondered if its accompanying decline in strength did not result from the vices of youth.

Samuel Johnson said his diseases were three: asthma, dropsy, and what was less curable—seventy-five years. Sir Clifford Albutt, with remarkably more prescience, said that we should not count the ages of people by the revolutions of the earth around the sun; rather we should measure them by the revolutions of their own morbid processes. In all of this there is an implied underlying theme—that only a few people know how to grow old and wear "age's silver livery gracefully," and that years alone do not make sages; they simply make men old.

As yet there is no general agreement as to what really constitutes senescence, but whether it is an inherent quality of germ plasm or a disease is really an academic question, for the aging problem is upon us in poignancy. André Repond, a contemporary Swiss physician, sees aging as one of life's biological crisis. In it sudden and rapid changes occur, resulting in a more or less permanent status. These crises are natural developments, he says, and they are inherent in life's processes.

---

*Nursing Homes, August 1963.

MAXIMAL DEVELOPMENT

Whichever of the multiple ideas alleged is eventually determined to be correct, several things are certain. At some point in life the tissues and energy reserves cease to expand; a maximal development is reached, an acme—and thence a gradual decline. Somewhere between the point of maximal expansion and the final end point, there is a period which denotes the onset of old age. This period is poorly marked and uncertain and often it is determined by the observer, by the measuring rod used, or by the purpose of the evaluation. Thus the deciding factor may be the degree of tissue degeneration, the industrial usefulness, or even the psychological or sociofamilial attitudes operative in the culture, rather than the exact chronologic age of the person.

Often certain essential functions of man are shaped by external events and often certain phases of senescence can be provoked and hastened by social forces; by loss of security, material or emotional; by isolation; or by feelings of uselessness. Only too frequently the elderly person finds himself exiled from the satisfactions of earlier years to a gray sort of no-man's land, alone, misunderstood and misunderstanding. In few aspects of my special field of medicine are the biological, the social, the psychological, and the pathological factors so sensitively attuned as they are in the emotional and the mental disorders of old age. We in the practice of medicine have had little to do with the social or economic segments of the problem; we have had much to do with the adding of years to human life, but one might wonder sometimes about the wisdom of this, if age is destined to be a regret, as Disraeli stated, or if the culture is to reject the aged and treat them badly.

GRADUAL IMPAIRMENT

Physiologically there occurs a gradual impairment of homeostatic capacities in older individuals, along with degenerative tissue changes. Emotional pressures in themselves play a part in the breakdown of homeostatis, for emotions, as well as toxins, can become psychonoxious. Old age is a time of unusual emotional stress. One by one the props of individual security vanish. The body image is distorted; the whole physical machine begins to sputter. The satisfactions of work and independence are missing now and the individual feels lost in a seemingly purposeless, hectic world. Companions of a life time are removed from the scene and the imminence of one's own exit may incite fear, rebellion, or even despair.

We make a mistake when we think of the older aged as a homogeneous group, however, for they are not. Some are rich and some are poor; some are sick and some are well; and most of them fall somewhere in between. Psychological and social pressures weigh heavily upon them, as they struggle vainly to retain roles beyond their competence and denied them for other reasons. Sources of gratification evaporate, yet personality needs are as strong as ever; they flow through channels cut long before.

The rigidity traditionally associated with old age is, in part, the expression of the need to maintain a world that used to be—a world in which self-esteem, satisfaction and relative mastery of the environment occurred at least some of the time. Inflexibility and a rigid life routine are sometimes adopted as defenses against this existential anxiety.

Frustration, disappointment, insecurity, organic impairment, all of these factors give rise to anxiety and each reinforces the other. Unless the personality retains sufficient integration to cope with the difficulties of aging and enough compensations are available to make up for the inevitable losses, morbid behavior may evidence itself. Shorn of prestige, bereft of old landmarks to adaptation, the aging individual may be prone to distort the environment in which he lives. The environment does not take kindly to this. Intolerance begets intolerance and the social climate may actually become as hostile as the individual has imagined it to be. As his problems increase, so does his incapacity. Evidences of senile change then begin to show themselves.

SENESCENCE

Until several decades ago anyone over the age of sixty to sixty-five who showed emotional or mental symptoms was *ipso facto* regarded as being senile or arteriosclerotic and therefore the knowledge is only recent that there is little correlation between the severity of organic brain changes and the degree of mental and

emotional dysfunction in senescence. Complexes which lead to forgetting are just as active in old age as they are in other periods of
life. The forgetting of proper names, for example, is often due
not only to lack of interest, but also to the fact that the memory is
repressed for some unconscious reason. It sometimes happens that
old people are hospitalized because of disorientation, confusion
and an apparent loss of retentive memory, looking for all the
world as though serious organic brain changes are operative; yet
under a program of attentive care and adequate stimulation the
failing faculties are soon restored. Therefore, even in senile de-
mentia presumably due to actual organic changes in the brain,
psychosociological factors are of great importance.

Lest we be too heavy about the recitation of some of these
depressive things, let us keep in mind the fact that we are looking
at this problem from an angle which is slightly skewed. All of those
wonderful people who have adjusted well fail to come under our
scrutiny. Hence the oppressive feeling about now in this discussion.
We have really seen only those individuals who have some kind
of emotional problem.

DEPRESSION

The psychiatrist is more and more impressed by the amount
of depression observed in the older age groups. There are, of
course, numerous and varied causes for this. There may be predis-
posing constitutional factors, situational stress, or various other
hidden vectors and it is often possible to arrest the march of these
depressions by means of psychotherapy associated with physical
treatment. Unfortunately, in the absence of a previous attack of
this kind, which would have altered both doctor and family, the
patients rarely come to medical attention until well after the depression has been established. Perhaps one of the most dramatic
advances in modern psychiatry is the rapid and successful treatment of depressive disorders. The plans for the future, so ably
commented upon by the President of the United States, seek to
capitalize upon this and other advances and to treat these patients
quickly and in the community, thus to prevent their abandonment
in large hospitals far from their homes.

There are some depressive states in senescence which have very deep roots, going back to early frustrations. Similar frustrating situations, notably abandonments, loss of dear and protective persons, poverty or its spectre, removal from accustomed habitat, placement in institution or home, can lead to profound feelings of helplessness and defeat. The person in later years is thus threatened from two sides at once—first by a realization of his declining forces; second by the attitude of society. It is difficult to be fully objective about advancing years, particularly because the different functions of the organism are affected quite irregularly.

INTOLERANCE

Moreover, old age is encircled by prejudices, taboos and ambivalent feelings. Individuals in the age group are expected to conform to the dignified images that people have of them. Taboos weigh heavily upon them, as does a general intolerance. People expect all of the virtues which other groups are not called upon to exhibit—wisdom, understanding, indulgence, absence of passion, and all of the essential virtues. As Emerson put it: "As you are old and reverend, you should also be wise." This image, no matter how unrealistic, is deeply anchored in the collective mind and there is a latent hostility toward the aged, which is easily externalized when an individual fails to exhibit the expected ideals of wisdom and dignity and behave in accordance with them at all times.

As far as this present culture is concerned, old people are no longer in the stream of things; it is youth and the potentialities of the future which monopolize people's attention. Older citizens are often actually impelled to draw into themselves—and this turning, unfortunately, often tends to fix attention upon one's physical health and to slip easily into psychosomatic disorders. Unconsciously there is hope that through symptoms and suffering they will receive the sympathy and attention which otherwise would not be accorded them. Even elementary attention and psychotherapy is of help here, providing it is an accompaniment of real human interest. Other patients in this group react rather badly; they are those of a more introverted nature, for this lends itself more easily to isolation. The final denouncement of this type of reaction is a ferocious narcissim which might easily lead to a break of all ties with reality.

Thus, the elderly person finds himself in a group which is poorly understood and resented, although this attitude is usually hidden beneath a superficial veneer of solicitude for its welfare. They are often pitied, but without real sympathy and feeling, by the younger age groups.

In a culture in which success is the *summum bonum* and financial condition the measure of that success the way of the transgressor who has not been "successful" is a difficult one. This apparently is not new, only its manifestation has changed. Seneca spoke of the disgrace of a man being able to produce no proof of his having lived long except his years. It is a bit more stark today, however, for the victim becomes the responsibility of the family and, as a recipient of their bounty, he loses caste, for he has failed to "measure up." Not only is this the family and community attitude, but it is also the one he acquires toward himself.

SOCIAL REJECTION

The fear of being unable to take care of one's self and of becoming a burden to others is a phobia ever present in the minds of many people because, as a consequence of it, they hazard social rejection and consequent loss of their own self-respect. Unfortunately, some rejection of the elderly is due to an unconscious fear that this will be the eventual lot of the rejector—this also lies behind some of the rejection of the mentally ill. Some of the social rejection has an aesthetic basis, for age sometimes brings with it a loss of social graces and carelessness in various spheres. Some of this is anything but lovely and the hostility which these characteristics engender is not always disguised. The consequent reaction only serves to drive the individual more and more into self-centered, irritable and resentful modes of behavior.

The attitudes of society are even magnified in the specific family situation. Here the resentment is enhanced by propinquity and is reinforced by feelings of guilt. Very real and practical problems confront the children who are sheltering these aged people but in the interest of time I shall not go deeply into them here. You know how the grandparent is shoved about; how the children take turns and keep a watchful eye on each other. You know, too, of the bitter quarrels between husband and wife and how marriages are threatened and some of them broken by the continued presence of an aged parent of one of them. There is no secret, either, about the emotional disharmony which may be rekindled on the basis of ancient conflicts between the aged parent and the son or daughter who is now providing the home. Long smouldering resentment over happenings far in the past may goad the children into domineering and hostile attitudes, with consequent quarrels, tears and hurt feelings.

Parents relinquish unwillingly positions of dominance once held in the family and this frequently incites clashes of opinion. At the same time aged parents have the universal need for love and acceptance and, when they become aware of familial rejection, they respond with a reaction pattern designed to re-establish inner security. This may take the form of temper tantrums or other attention seeking behavior or, in other cases, the aged person may adopt aggressive behavior to make sure he is not overlooked. These efforts failing, depression, illness, discouragement or complete isolation are all that are left. Suicidal gestures, or even successful suicide, may be next.

Suicide is the eleventh leading cause of death in the United States and its incidence is highest in the aged. Depressed patients are often potentially suicidal. The British journal, *The Lancet,* says these gestures are a kind of Russian Roulette in which the patient is prepared to gamble the chance of losing his life against the possibility that things will improve if he survives. (They often do.) Thus, the possibility of suicide must always be kept in mind, especially in the depressed patient who sees no reason for going on and who has convinced himself that his departure would make it easier for others.

JOBS AND RETIREMENT

The aged find that the modern economic and industrial technological schemes have no place for them. With the exception of some skilled trades and professions, workers more than forty years of age are not wanted. Thus, men are discarded vocationally and rendered economically impotent and unproductive by factors beyond their control. There are other important implications in having a job, aside from the financial security it affords. The individual is given prestige in his own eyes and a feeling of social approval. He feels he was a place in the busy work-a-day world and it is probable that this feeling is even more important than financial return. The loss of this ability to contribute and earn respect demeans an individual in his own estimation. For this reason many elderly men "hang on," much to the annoyance of their younger colleagues. Even though they "putter," their duties are of extreme importance because they preserve for the individual the sense of belonging.

There is a great deal of pressure in labor and in industry to get rid of the older worker and now retirement is one of the poignant facts of life. Numerous plans are in operation—some of them intricate—to soften the blow. Psychologically it is a blow, no matter how well prepared one is for it to occur. Separation, anxiety at first and depression later are frequent concomitants to the cutting off of an individual for a job, which, while he may have complained about it, yet he considered his own. Some men adapt to it willingly; more unwillingly; and some not at all. The first group is blessed; the middle group constitutes the irritable and the difficult; and the third group contributes of its number to the rank of the depressed.

MENTAL HYGIENE

There is a danger always in discussing the psychological aspects of aging—a danger that it be a recital of lugubrious and depressing ideas and events . This attitude is not justifiable, for many men in the older age groups are in extremely important government positions, both at home and abroad; others are active in the professions and unaware of the weight of years. They are living proof of Doctor Albutt's dictum that age is not to be reckoned by the number of revolutions of the earth around the sun. In that this meeting is directed toward improving the health care of the aged, let us see what, if anything, of a preventive nature can be done to prevent or alleviate some of the distressing things that we have had to enumerate.

Although it sounds fatuous, it is true that the best preparation for meeting the problems of declining years is sound mental hygiene in earlier life. The dictum of Cephalus in Plato's *Philo-*

sophy of Old Age is obviously true: "The Truth is, Socrates, that these regrets and also the complaints about relations are to be attributed to the same cause, which is not old age but men's characters and tempers; for he who is of calm and happy nature will hardly feel the pressure of age, but to him who is of an opposite disposition youth and age are equally a burden."

Though the physician cannot change the nation's retirement laws, cultural patterns, or the economic situation of the country, he can be of assistance in advising those who are interested in the plight of the elderly. What is it that separates the elderly with non-organic conditions and closes them off from the stream of things? For the most part it seems to be a loss of communication with their surroundings. Frequently beset with problems, they neglect to keep up with the times. As they dislocate themselves in time, their standards and symbols lose meaning and there is a pathetic clinging to values to which these symbols were once appropriate.

The first rule of mental hygiene in aging, therefore, is keeping open the channels of communication. It is insurance against getting lost and out of contact with younger age groups and with daily happenings. Also, one might heed the admonition of the psalmist: "A joyful mind maketh age flourishing; a sorrowful spirit drieth up the bones." The watchword is that one must have something—some interest, some responsibility, some task—which will make him feel useful and feel that he is a part of things. Without this, the person will just sit.

The second axiom should be spread broadcast, namely that there is no necessary parallel between chronological and psychological old age. The maxim: "You are as old as you feel or think," has much to commend it. We have already noted that autopsy often reveals brain changes which should have spelled senile psychosis; yet the patient carried on in a responsible position right up to the end. The opposite of this is also true. Many senile manifestations are based upon the fact that the person has given up, has quit, and has failed to stay in the stream of current events for some reason unrecognized even by himself. Some people are even adversely affected consciously by the passage of time—a calendar neurosis which has serious consequences; they are allergic to that stark phrase, "three score years and ten." This seeking out of a seat on the sidelines of life is demoralizing and the task of mental hygiene is to prevent it.

Thirdly, serious preparation must be made for retirement. Some industries and professional groups are already hard at these preparations. Would that we all could approach retirement as did the Chinese poet, T'oo Chien, who said:

"I am free from ties and can live the life of retirement. When I rise from sleep I play with books and the harp."

Later he adds:

"Self-support should maintain strict limits. More than enough is not what I want."

And finally:

"These things have made me happy again. And I forget my lost cap of office."

Unfortunately, far from forgetting the lost cap of office, most of us cannot even remove it. The need for the development of outside interests by men and women near retirement age is pressing and may even be life-saving.

NUMEROUS INTERESTS

Dr. Willia Shepard observes that very few people are one-interest persons and almost everybody has numerous interests, if only they can be encouraged to develop them.[1] He speaks of one industry which has eighteen classes running for various hobbies, running nine months a year. The classes are held from 5:15 p.m. to 6:45 p.m. and are taught by experts. Some employees become so expert that they supplement their income by means of their hobbies.

There are those who know much more about this aspect of things than do I, so I shall only make one comment about the use of hobbies. As a clinician, I am in a position to see that idleness is demoralizing, as is excess leisure. We must be on guard that our increased leisure, due to shorter work weeks, does not lead us to malignant boredom, for this in itself is a medium in which mental disorder might flourish.

REMINISCENCE

A recent paper, entitled "The Life Review—An Interpretation of Reminiscence in the Aged," is of interest to us here.[2] The author, Dr. R. N. Butler, feels that a mental process of reviewing one's life is universal in older people. This process helps account for the increased reminiscence that we recognize so well and contributes to the occurrence of certain late-life disorders, particularly depression; and it participates also in the evolution of such characteristics as candor, serenity, and wisdom among certain of the aged.

As the past marches in review it is surveyed, observed and reflected upon by the ego. Reconsideration of previous experiences and their meaning occurs often with revised and expanded understanding. Such reorganization may give a more valid picture, giving new and significant meaning to one's life. It may also mitigate fear of death. It seems, he says, that in a majority of the elderly a substantial reorganization of the personality occurs. This may help to account for the evolution of such qualities as the wisdom and serenity, already mentioned. There are many other qualities, memories and fantasies which may be brought up in these reviews—some of them tragic—but we have listened to enough of that and we would prefer to end on a somewhat more pleasant note.

It has been said that, as we get older, our bodies get shorter but our anecdotes get longer; so I shall be very careful and will try to draw just one or two practical points from what we have discussed. First, this life review mentioned by Dr. Butler intrigues me. There is sure to come a time in it, or even now, when we realize that the image we think we project is not the one seen by the public or our friends. The image which we think of as kindness and righteousness may be seen as gruffness, unpleasantness, or even destructiveness. It is probably wise to pause for a moment and catch a glimpse of that image as a reality factor—we may have to do some rearranging of our present approach to things.

Next, and finally, the advice given by the Provost of the General Practitioners in England regarding the emotionally distressed is applicable for all who treat the aged:

> "Their greatest sin is that they take too much of the doctor's time. But insufficient time to treat them is no excuse for an unsympathetic or an irritable manner. We should always try to have a few minutes to spare each day for the lonely person who wants to be talked to, to be advised, or even quite often to be instructed. A dismissal after ten minutes of chatting is far more

effective and lasting than a hurried prescription after two minutes of reproach. And to descend for a moment to the commercial, remember that neurotics will be your best advertisement or your worst. Willy-nilly they constitute the group of people who talk the most; it is nice to arrange that they say the right things.[3]"

Finally, it does seem that this advice is too good to be reserved entirely for family doctors; we all might benefit, and older folks might benefit, if we appropriated some it it for ourselves.

REFERENCES

1. SHEPARD, WILLIAM P.: Retirement from the viewpoint of a medical director. *Industrial Medicine and Surgery.29:*7, 309-314, July 1960.
2. BUTLER, ROBERT N., M.D.: The life review—an interpretation of reminiscence in the aged. *Psychiatry, 26:*65, 1963.
3. GIBSON, RONALD, Provost SE England Faculty, College of General Practice: Introducing the family doctor. *Lancet,* Aug. 27, 1955.

THE MEANING OF RELIGION TO OLDER PEOPLE*

Nila Kirkpatrick Covalt, M.D.

T HE BODY OF THIS PAPER was first presented on a panel entitled "The Meaning of Religion to Older Persons" at the Florida Council on Aging in 1958. The experiences of a physician were thought to be rich and informative on this subject. I was asked to participate in the panel, and I was glad to accept the assignment. After twenty-five years of practice, I knew that my experiences in this regard would come as a surprise. The opportunity was presented to express some general facts, correct some fallacies, and, perhaps, suggest some constructive criticism. Necessarily, the opinions expressed must be given with much personal and local reference.

For eleven years and including all of World War II, I was in general practice. Since then, my practice has been limited entirely to the special field of physical medicine and rehabilitation. The general practice period, which was in my home town of Muncie, Indiana, represents an over-all approach to illness. The specialty offers experience in devastating, often sudden and catastrophic physical handicaps that often affect older persons. A very large per cent of my experience in this specialty has been with older people.

The remark has often been made that "people turn to religion as they grow older." In my experience, I have not been aware of this fact. Neither have I known people to turn to religion when they are seriously ill, the victims of a catastrophic illness, or severely or even permanently physically handicapped. I am in-

*Geriatrics, 15:658-664, September 1960.

clined to think that the statement is empirical and should be evaluated with a true statistical study and numerous samplings.

During my medical career, I can recall no patient who chose to discuss his religious beliefs or problems with me. I have never heard my colleagues mention that their patients discussed these problems with them, either, although surely this has been the case in isolated instances. Although I have not checked every reference on the subject, I doubt whether any textbook on psychosomatic medicine contains a separate discussion on religion.

Sickness is not a time for delusion or a time to correct a person's attitudes toward the hereafter, but it is, or perhaps can be, a time to strengthen his faith. My personal opinion is that religion is a private matter and a subject an individual is more likely to talk about with his minister if he talks with anyone. A person may labor under delusions just because he is ill and realizes that he is not impervious to illness or even, at times, to a very radical change in body image, such as an amputation of an extremity. A patient needs to have confidence and faith in his doctor or doctors if he is to make a maximum response and adjustment. If he is ridden with doubts about his recovery and to that is added guilt feelings as well as worry about the hereafter, the psychosomatic aspects of his illness are enhanced.

Modern religion has changed from the dogmas and doctrines of "hell-fire and damnation," to that of brotherhood. The modern clergyman is an enlightened leader, a man of faith, and a friend. He probably feels about religion much as the doctor does. There are probably as many concepts of a deity or the here-after as there are individuals. The concepts of a primitive man would bear no relationship to the ideas of an intellectual person today. The range of thinking is so vast that it is doubtful whether any person's concept changes just because he has become ill.

VARIETIES OF EXPERIENCE

We physicians have learned that when a patient brings a Bible with him to the hospital and keeps it displayed, this action is a sign of anticipated trouble from an insecure individual. The stable, secure individual who is in civic and church life of the community seldom brings his Bible to the hospital.

The insecure individuals frequently proved to be members of small offshoot religious sects, the "fringe" groups from struggling little churches on the outskirts of the city or in the poorer areas.

These patients caused trouble to themselves and their physicians in a variety of ways. They were uncooperative and did not, or could not, carry out instructions or be taught to do so. They fought the nurses and complained about even the smallest matters and generally, in one way or another, hindered their recovery.

"Ma" Wells is the best example of such a patient. Caring for her was a cross I bore for eleven years, and, in spite of all the problems she presented, she was kept alive for several more years by the doctors who succeeded me. A severe diabetic who needed insulin, neither she nor her husband could ever be made to understand about her diet. She phoned the office almost every day, but either she or "Pa" never failed to phone the house every Sunday at either 11:00 or 11:30 a.m. to ask if she could have pie or some dessert for that Sunday's dinner. It was a rare month, while three constituted a prize, that I did not have to rush her into the hospital for impending diabetic coma or some other complication of her disease. I never heard of her attending any church, but she always brought her Bible to the hospital. She was so unpleasant to the nurses that they often threatened to leave unless I discharged her at once.

A patient of a far different and organized religious belief, in which group she had always been very active, came to me in the eighth month of her first pregnancy. She had not seen a doctor before. She was over forty. She had gained 100 pounds and her blood pressure was over 200. Obviously, she was eclamptic and just ready to go into convulsions. Immediately hospitalized, of course, the convulsions started three days later. An immediate version extraction of the baby had to be attempted by the obstetrician whom I had already called in consultation after my first examination. To add to the situation, the woman had a double uterus and the baby was in the second one that the obstetricians entered. The child was already dead and was also under the viable weight of two pounds.

Four hours after delivery, the patient died in convulsions, and such a commotion I have never heard. The twelve or more relatives and friends who gathered shrieked at the top of their lungs for two hours and said the woman was not dead. Every time we tried to prepare the body to move it out of the room, someone would tear the sheet back and insist that the woman was not dead. The nurses and I could not make these people leave the floor. Another doctor who came by was also unable to do anything. Our appeals about concern for the other women in that wing meant nothing. Finally, by 2:00 a.m., after routing the superintendent out of bed at her home five miles away, she was able to persuade them to leave. There was no prayer involved in this hysteria.

On the other side of the picture was an old friend of mine and of my parents who was their age. She was a quiet, unassuming churchgoer who never spoke of religion but who I knew was active in many church activities. An emergency decompression of her brain became necessary on Sunday. My two professors of neurosurgery from medical school had been called in for the diagnosis and to perform the surgery.

After the operation, it was a "touch and go" proposition for several hours, and I stayed beside her during that time. The next morning she had recovered more than any of us had anticipated. She said to me, "I was in heaven yesterday and you called me back. I am grateful to you, for I still want to live awhile."

She is still alive and now in her eighties. On last report, more than fifteen years since her operation, she has been working twenty-four hours a day on two shifts. During the daytime, she cares for a woman who is also in her eighties and then goes to the home of a ninety-two-year-old woman whom she looks after during the night.

There is no way to know or understand what this woman went through in her unconscious, subconscious, or post-anesthetic state. As people are regaining consciousness, many seem to experience various thoughts, or even visions, just as one does in dreams. These experiences may at times be of great spiritual significance to the individual, and his life may be greatly affected by them. If so, any discussion about them probably takes place with his minister or a psychiatrist.

I can recall no patient in twenty-five years who ever asked me to call his minister for him. Perhaps the reason why my patients never asked me to call their ministers was because almost every minister made routine, daily hospital visits to his parishioners. If a doctor was working with a patient, the clergyman usually waited outside the room until the doctor and the nurse were through. However, at times even a "No Visitors" sign failed to keep a minister from walking in without having discussed his prerogative to do so with the doctor.

THE MINISTER'S CALL

It seems to me that there are two ways in which a minister should visit the sick. One is professionally; the other is as a friend. I believe that clergymen should call upon members of their church who are ill either at home or in the hospital only when the patient has asked him to do so unless the minister and patient are friends. I also think that relatives should not ask a clergyman to call unless they are sure that the patient has agreed to the professional visit. In addition, it seems to me that a "No Visitors" sign includes a minister unless he has had special permission from the doctor to see the patient.

I have seen a patient wilt before my eyes when a minister walked in unexpectedly. I think that many patients no matter how religious they may be, want to set their own time to contemplate matters of the spirit. The modern minister is no longer the symbol of death or a person who goes around pointing an accusing finger and administering prayer to "prepare for eternity." The intelligent person does not think of him in that light today, but he still may harbor some individual ideologies or concepts that he does not want to contemplate while he is ill. The same situation may be even more true when patients are about to undergo surgery. Surely, any person who must have an operation faces this ordeal with varying amounts of fear. Keeping a "stiff upper lip" and not outwardly acknowledging these fears often help. The patient who breaks down and cries and the relatives who gather around and weep with him just before surgery improve no one's state of mind. If a minister arrives at such a time to remind them of the spirit, the direness of the situation is sometimes accentuated.

I knew one minister who made it a point of trying to see all of his parishioners who were going to surgery *after* they had been given preanesthetic medication. He could not be kept out of the rooms. Needless to say, his parishioners arrived in surgery wide awake, apprehensive, and with their normal fears accentuated. When any of us had a patient whom we knew was one of his parishioners, we tried to outwit him and keep him away, but he usually slipped by us, even at times walking by the stretcher and talking. None of the doctors cared to take the responsibility of ordering him away, although perhaps someone should have. I am afraid that this minister had little or no concept of the physiologic responses of the body to emotion, but his intentions were the very best.

EXPERIENCE WITH THE PHYSICALLY HANDICAPPED

In another hospital in New England, where I worked for several years with the physically handicapped, the population was predominately Roman Catholic, as it was in the hospital where I interned. The priest or priests were always in attendance in both. The latter state-operated hospital had 250 beds plus a 500-bed domiciliary home where veterans could live as long as they liked with their expenses paid by the state. Some of these men had lived there at least since World War I. Most of the domiciliary residents had been misfits in society; few had ever earned much, if any, living. Some who had families had abandoned them. The average age fluctuated between fifty-five to sixty-four. The age was dropping when I left because young, World War II veterans were moving in to make their home there. There were few native born New Englanders. The majority were first and second generation Europeans from nations which are predominately considered Roman Catholic. The resident priest used to stop in my office to bewail the fact that the attendance at all of his masses each Sunday never totaled more than twenty-five. The Protestant minister, a nonresident, told me that he had ten or twelve in his Sunday congregation.

The priest had a great deal of enthusiasm, a "joie de vivre," and an outgoing personality. He had been a Navy chaplain on ship in the South Pacific which had been under fire and kamikaze attack. Furthermore, while on this assignment, he had been one of the survivors of a terrible plane crash in New Jersey. Though badly burned himself, he was credited with having saved several lives. There was no reason why, as a man among men, this priest should not have been able to get along well with his all male congregation. It is probably a logical conclusion to assume that the men in the domiciliary home had been misfits all their lives. Even their early Catholic training had failed to remain an influence in their lives.

Several hundred severely handicapped men went through a full program of *rehabilitation* in our Physical Medicine and Rehabilitation Department of this hospital. There were over 200 amputees, most of whom were over sixty. Most of these amputations had been done after many weeks of circulatory disturbances of the legs, so that the majority of the men who underwent such operations had had time to adjust their thinking to their change in body image. We treated even more patients who had had strokes than we did amputees. The greatest per cent of these patients maintained their mental acuity.

There used to be fifteen to twenty-five amputees and twenty-five to thirty-five hemiplegics under training at all times and, in addition, ten to twenty had had spinal cord injuries. Most often the cord lesions were complete, and many were at the cervical level. Certainly, this kind of lesion with the loss of sensation, loss of bladder and bowel control as well as loss of muscle control is as dramatic and devastating a disability as can be had. It usually requires months to adjust to the emotional impact of such a situation.

Of all this group, I recall only one, an Italian Catholic, in whom the cord had been completely severed, who needed and asked for religious help. His emotional adjustment was long and hazardous, and there were several occasions when we feared he would commit suicide. The priest, the psychiatrist, my staff and I, and all the nurses and other doctors who had any contact with this man worked with him for many months before he became reconciled and completed his program of physical rehabilitation.

Another man in his forties had had polio which had paralyzed both legs, and sufficient time had elapsed so that all muscle power had returned that could be expected to return. He had intimated that as soon as he was discharged he was going to St. Anne de Beaupré where he would be cured. Two weeks after his discharge, he returned to the hospital with his long-leg steel braces so badly twisted that they were beyond repair. Since he refused to tell us what happened, we could only hazard the guess that he might have crawled all the way to the top of the steps at St. Anne's and then lost his balance and rolled all the way down. His paralysis was the same. The other Italian Catholic paraplegic is, we understand, continuing to make annual pilgrimages to St. Anne de Beaupré, although his injury occurred in 1948.

These were the only two patients in that hospital whom I can remember who brought religion up at any time. I recall no such instances from my experience in New York or now in Florida.

COOPERATION OF PHYSICIANS AND MINISTERS

Let me emphasize that none of these isolated situations are to be taken as generalizations or as implied criticism of the clergy. Ministers and doctors are as human as everyone else. Individual problems among them, as among others, are usually due to a lack of understanding and, even more important, a lack of adequate communication between the people concerned. Doctors welcome the ministers' help. I feel sure that the ministers' visits are most often helpful. Were a census to be taken, I suspect that it would reveal that most physicians are church members and personal friends of ministers of more than one denomination and that they attend church whenever their practices permit.

I have presented almost every situation that I can recall in which religion was the factor during an illness. The paucity of these experiences from a doctor's viewpoint suggests that, if a person who is ill asks for and wants more spiritual help at that time, his physician is not made aware of his request. I recall no person who called out to God or audibly prayed when he knew he was dying. Usually, these persons are exerting every bit of energy in a struggle to keep alive. I do not believe my experiences are different from those of other physicians.

It seems to be a rather general opinion that most persons do ask for more spiritual help when they are seriously ill. Might I suggest that this may be another empirical statement that should be questioned. I do not have any idea whether the majority of sick people do privately ask their pastors for more help at this time or whether some ministers simply presume this to be true and proceed on that premise. This is a question that the ministers themselves would have to answer.

PATTERNS OF WORSHIP

As I said earlier, I do think that the saying "people turn to religion as they grow older" is a fallacy. It is possible that one empirical statement follows into another because aging and illness are so commonly thought of as synonymous terms. Old age and chronic illness do increase at a proportionally more rapid rate as people age and, while our aging population has increased so very rapidly, some very recent figures show that the percentage of older people with chronic disease is not proportional to the rising number of cases of all persons with chronic illness. Two-fifths of chronically ill persons are over sixty-five, one-third are middle-aged, and one and one-half million are children, not including those who are mentally defective.

The attitude of most older people about religion is probably most often that with which they grew up or which they have accepted as they achieved intellectual maturity. Patterns of worship and of church attendance have remained much the same or have been modified by circumstances which, to the individual, are logical modifications.

Several years ago, old or aging persons might suddenly have become interested in religion and joined a church because churches generally stressed doctrines that were concerned with salvation. An older person even might have joined a church late in life for his "fire insurance" as someone so aptly put it.

There is an all-time high percentage of church members in the United States at this time. The broadening of church attitudes is probably the biggest reason to account for this. If a broad statistical study were made, I am inclined to think that the older person who joins a church for the first time or returns to church because he is growing older and feels the need of more spiritual help would be in the minority.

Had time permitted before presenting this paper, I should have liked to have asked some ministerial associations to make a report on the actual percentage of older persons who are now joining their churches. I only had the opportunity to discuss the matter with one minister. He graciously agreed to go through his records, even though there was little time to check all ages accurately. He reported that 553 people had joined his church between October 31, 1955, and March 31, 1958. Of these, he reported that three adults had been baptized who were sixty years of age or over. He was also sure of fifty-two members "who had been received either on profession of faith—uniting with the church for the first time—or who had made a reaffirmation of faith after a long absence." More such surveys in several communities should be interesting as well as valuable.

Any contributions that I have made on the subject of religion from the standpoint of a physician appear to be on the negative side. It would certainly be informative if other physicians expressed their personal experiences in this regard. I believe those persons who first asked me to discuss this matter expected an accounting of rich experience in this field. I accepted the invitation knowing that I could not, in a positive way, produce the wealth of information that was expected.

Doctors generally do not believe that they have the right to probe into the spiritual life of their patients except in special instances and situations. The fact that I can present no evidence of a real knowledge of increased religious yearnings in older people who have been patients may, if confirmed, be a very positive fact that will remove one fallacy, at least, from our thinking. In writing thus, I did not mean to disappoint nor find an opportunity to criticize or generalize, but I welcomed the chance to pose these questions. I do hope that my remarks offer a point at which to start some further study.

PATIENTS WHO GROW OLD IN A MENTAL HOSPITAL*

Robert Sommer, Ph.D.

Discussions of the condition of geriatric patients in mental hospitals often concern themselves with the recent increase in admission rates for people over sixty. However, of equal importance to mental hospital administrators are those patients who have grown old in the hospital. While some administrators feel that the first group of elderly patients are not primarily their concern, none will deny their responsibility for the second group. These well institutionalized patients are living longer and changing the complexion of hospitals throughout North America. Our older nurses recall that when Saskatchewan Hospital opened thirty-five years ago, only a handful of patients were over sixty; now fully 40 per cent are in this age group. This has had repurcussions in all hospital departments, ranging from physical medicine to nurses' training to recreation. For example, the hospital had previously aimed at a nursing staff composed solely of fully qualified psychiatric nurses. But with the increase of spoon-feeding, bed changing, and other tasks required on geriatric wards, pressure has been exerted to hire more nurses' aides. The physical medicine department has increased in both number and importance with the influx of geriatric patients. In essence, not only have the tactics of individual wards been changed but also the strategy of the provincial psychiatric services system.

A number of articles have vividly described the shortage of community geriatric centers. Along with the trend toward smaller houses and longer life expectancy, this is one of the factors contri-

*Geriatrics, 14:581-590, September 1959.

buting to the increased admission of geriatric patients to mental hospitals. Horbaczewski, for example, showed that of 280 patients over sixty admitted to this hospital during 1955-6, two-thirds were suffering from clinical conditions *without* psychoses.[1] However, the present paper is concerned with the second category of geriatric patients, those who have grown old in a mental hospital. We hope to summarize some of the findings from a several-year investigation of the effects of long-term hospitalization upon their values, skills, and family relationships.

First, it may be useful to show the magnitude of the problem. On the basis of a 12 per cent random sample of all patients in this hospital, it was shown that approximately 35 per cent had been in hospital twenty years or longer. If the lengths of stay of all patients presently in the hospital were averaged (summing multiple admissions), the resulting figure is sixteen years. In 1952 a study of the total patient population (100 per cent sample) showed that the median length of stay was twelve years. Hence the results of our sample seven years later seem reasonably accurate. At Warren State Hospital, Morgan and Nelson found the median length of stay of all chronic patients to be eleven years.[2] However, they used only the duration of *last* hospitalization and pointed out that the sum of all admissions for each patient would yield a figure much higher than eleven years.

ESTIMATES OF PATIENTS' HOSPITALIZATION

To learn to what extent the hospital staff was aware of the composition of the patient population, we conducted a small survey in which people were asked to estimate both the average length of stay for all patients and the percentage of patients in each five-year range. That is, various staff members were asked:

1) We are interested in learning what you think is the average length of hospitalization of all patients presently in the hospital. That is, if you averaged how long every one of the present patients have been in the hospital, how long would it be?

2) What percent of our present patient population has been in the hospital:

Less than a year?
From one to five years?

From five to ten years?
Ten to fifteen years?
Fifteen to twenty years?
Twenty to twenty-five years?
More than twenty-five years?

The answers showed clearly that most of the staff members greatly underestimated the average length of stay. The median estimates for each of the groups are presented in Table 1 with the figures based on the random sample.

Many of the answers were surprising. A supervisor on a geriatric ward where the average length of stay was over twenty years estimated that only 2 per cent of the patients had been in the hospital over twenty-five years. Several staff members whose work kept them on admission wards estimated that one-half of the patients were in the hospital less than five years. The hospital secretaries, with the exception of one who was attached to social service, had only the vaguest idea of the average length of stay.

Explanations of this are not difficult to find. Probably two factors are chiefly responsible: the emphasis on admission ward work for many staff members and the fact that most patients have been here longer than the average staff member. Often when a supervisor was asked how long an individual patient had been in hospital, he would reply, "Well, he has been here as long as

TABLE 1
MEDIAN ESTIMATES OF LENGTH OF HOSPITILIZATION

	Psychiatrists N = 9	Social Workers N = 6	Student Nurses N = 9	Senior Nurses N = 10	Stenos N = 7	Random Sample N = 191
Average (in years), for all patients	7.5	8.5	10	6.5	4	16
Per cent of patients in hospital: less than 5 years	32	43	17	40	50	24
5—10 years	15	18	15	15	10	13
10—15 years	20	17	15	15	10	10
15—20 years	15	10	15	13	10	14
20—25 years	10	7	10	8	10	14
more than 25 years	5	5	13	5	10	24

I have, anyway." In one sense the patients are the "culture car-riers" of the hospital. It is they who provide the continuity to ward life. Not only have most nurses been in hospital less time than their patients, they are more frequently shifted from one ward to another.

To learn more specifically the length of time "in hospital" of staff members, we drew a one-third random sample of the nursing department. We computed the total time that each nurse had worked in any mental hospital (here or elsewhere). We find the greatest difference at the ends of the curves. Sixty-five per cent of the nurses have been in hospital less than five years as against 25 per cent of the patients, while 38 per cent of the patients have been in hospital longer than twenty years as against 3 per cent of the staff.

ESTIMATES OF PATIENTS' ABILITIES

Another illustration of this lack of knowledge regarding long-stay patients came in a study of "mute" patients on a very regressed male ward. We became interested in this ward when we encoun-tered several nurses who believed that less than half the patients would answer even a simple question. We designed a small study whereby each of two student nurses was given a list of thirty names, chosen at random from the ward roster. The nurse was requested to approach each patient on the list and ask the follow-ing three questions, waiting twenty seconds for a reply:

1. It's a nice day, isn't it?
2. What is your name?
3. What day of the week is it?

The results showed that 87 per cent of the patients answered question 1; 89 per cent answered question 2; while 81 per cent gave an appropriate answer to question 3. This demonstrated that it was incorrect for nurses to assume that patients who rarely or never talk would not talk if approached.

NEGLECT OF CASE FILES

This lack of familiarity with long-stay patients is also reflected in the use of case files by staff members. Pollitt cites a study by

Smith[3] where it was found that the case files on many long-stay patients were very inadequate. Some had not been taken from the file room for a period of years. The author concluded, "The longer the patient was in the hospital, the less likely the staff was to know about him." When one remembers the high turnover among hospital personnel, such as the 70 per cent annual rate for physicians at the hospital studied by Belknap,[4] this is quite understandable. Moore believes that in the same way that familiar objects are taken

TABLE 2
LENGTH OF LAST HOSPITALIZATION OF DECEASED PATIENTS AT VARIOUS
AGE LEVELS

	Age at Death:			
	Less than 60	*60-70*	*70-80*	*More than 80*
Median years in hospital	12	7	3	1
Number of cases	(8)	(17)	(44)	(31)

for granted, long-stay patients become so much a part of the hospital that they get lost in the place and remain year after year.[5] In this hospital we examined the records for the use of case histories. We found that, during a one-month period, the case histories of 299 patients had been signed out of the file room. (Many others had been read in the file room, and a large number of histories had been borrowed several times.) These had been signed out for a variety of reasons, ranging from eligibility to pension rights, physical illness, and social service placement to securing data for a research project. When we checked to see how long these 299 patients had been in hospital as compared with the total hospital population, we found an over-representation of short-stay patients (less than a year) and an under-representation of long-stay patients.

HOSPITAL MORTALITY RATE

Another important facet to the situation of the long-stay patient is the hospital mortality rate. Kramer and associates maintain that in all age levels mental hospital mortality rates are higher than in the general population.[6] However it is important to learn whether more deaths occur in the long-stay group or in the recent admission. In order to obtain some information on this matter, we examined the records for the last 100 deaths in the hospital. These were compared with the figures for the last 100 deaths in the local health region—that is, nearby town and surrounding area.

The age curves show that the age-mortality relationship in hospital and community is similar, although proportionally more death occur in the younger group in the outside community. Thirty-two per cent of deaths occurred within the first year of admission and 57 per cent occurred within the first five years. The majority of deaths, then, occurred in the recently admitted group rather than the long-stay patients.

An even clearer picture emerges when the ages of the deceased patients are compared with the lengths of their most recent hospitalization. This is summarized in Table 2, which shows that the younger deceased patients had been in hospital far longer than the older deceased patients. In fact, deceased patients over eighty averaged less than a year in hospital while deceased patients under sixty averaged twelve years.

The very detailed follow-up study by Malzberg adds further data on this point.[7] He showed that, of patients over seventy years of age admitted to New York State mental hospital, 59 per cent died within the first year. He also found that after the second year in hospital, the death rate stabilized at a very low level.

DISCULTURATION

Many of the effects of long-term hospitalization are not noticeable on a day-to-day basis, but, if one compares patients who have been here for varying periods, its influence becomes apparent. In our work, we use the concept of *disculturation* to understand these changes in attitude and skill over time. Disculturation occurs when a patient learns values and attitudes which unsuit him for the culture from which he came or to which he is going. This applies not only to hospital patients but to any situation where people must live in a society whose norms and values differ from those of their previous community. Former prisoners of war, displaced persons, convicts, and residents of TB sanitoria may be markedly discultured when they return to their former homes.

We may briefly cite some of the difficulties encountered by

returning prisoners or mental patients. One hospital found that recently paroled patients made great sport of crossing the street with traffic signals, as they had never seen signals before. Another hospital found that its patients knew nothing about the dial telephones and bus transfers. Vermont State Hospital found that its patients needed instruction on personal hygiene and grooming, reacquaintance with money value, and familarization with modern household equipment. For example, women who had been confined for a long time found it confusing when they tried to perform household chores. The only products they had used in the hospital came in industrial sized packages. They needed experience with cleaning agents in quantities suitable for household use. They also found it difficult to adjust to new sleeping hours, since they had been accustomed to going to bed at 8 p.m. and rising at 6 a.m. Recently released patients also complained about the speed and quantity of traffic. Auto horns and fast-moving cars were particularly frightening. Parking meters were a mystery to many patients.

Nathan Leopold mentions how taking one's silverware from the table and depositing it at the rear of the dining room becomes so ingrained in the life of the prisoner that many have been embarrassed after release to find themselves picking up silverware at a home or restaurant and beginning to walk out with it.[8] Elkin mentions how prisoners lose all capacity to make independent decisions.[9] Johnson states that one of the worst effects of imprisonment is the sense of social degradation it instills in the prisoner.[10] Curle found the former POW's were unable to accept the cultural validity of their former civilian roles, as they felt separated from family and friends by a wide gulf of experience impossible to share.[11]

Disculturation is found even in retreats and sanctuaries for creative artists. The Huntington Hartford Foundation has a policy that no artist or musician can remain for more than six months in any two-year period. They found that those who stay longer are likely to lose their contacts at home and find it difficult to re-establish themselves. Several authors have alluded to the "institutionalitis" of prison guards and hospital nurses due to their isolation from the mainstream of community life. It is interesting to note that what we have termed "disculturation" is discussed by many authors under various headings. Along with "institutionalization" we find "hospitalitis," "desocialization", and "prisonization."

In this hospital, much of our research has been concerned with the effects of long-term hospitalization upon the patient's contact with the outside world. A study of patients who receive visitors showed that the longer the patient remained in hospital, the less likely he was to receive visitors.[12] It is interesting to note that this relationship is independent of the patient's age. That is, a newly admitted older patient is just as likely to receive visitors as a newly admitted younger patient. In this respect, we see a marked difference between the newly admitted elderly patient and the elderly patients who have aged in hospital.

An equally striking relationship was found when we studied the patients who wrote and received letters. The longer a patient had been in the hospital, the less likely he was to send or receive letters.[13]

In another study, Nettler's scale of social alienation was administered to patients who had been in the hospital for varying periods.[14] The scale indicates how closely a person's values conform to those of the dominant culture outside (for example, whether he likes TV, the *Reader's Digest,* new model cars, and so on). The results disclosed that patients on the longer stay wards were more deviant in their values than patients on the admission ward.[15]

RATING OF NEEDS

To learn more specifically the values that become altered during long-term hospitalization, we asked patients and staff the question "What is important to you?" Each person was requested to give three answers. The subjects were twenty-two patients on long-stay or geriatric wards, fifty-four patients on active treatment wards, and eighteen patients on admission wards. The control subjects were fifty members of the hospital staff, almost all in subprofessional categories, such as workmen, plumbers, and stenographers. The groups were evenly divided as to sex, but, since no large sex difference was found, the scores from both sexes were combined. The responses were scored as falling into one of the following categories:

A. Physical needs (for example, eating, sleeping, sex).
B. Vocational needs (for example, my job, cooking, my education).
C. Recreational needs: involve doing (for example, social activities, sewing, TV).
D. Social-religious needs: people, things, entities, organizations (for example, family, home, my possessions, religion).
E. Abstract goals: no specific referents (for example, happiness in general, fame, money, helping others).
F. Situational needs: specific to present situation (for example, discharge, nurses).
G. Miscellaneous.

Two raters working independently did the scoring. A reliability check on sixty-seven responses showed 95 per cent agreement. Before comparing the results from the various groups, we decided to omit the situational (hospital) responses which comprised 9 per cent of the patients responses, as they would have artificially inflated the differences between patient and staff groups. We also omitted miscellaneous responses because the number (2 per cent) was negligible.

The results disclosed that the responses of the patient group differed significantly ($x^2 = 54$, df $= 4$, p$<$.001) from those of the staff group. When the patients were classified as to ward, we find that there were no significant differences between staff and admission ward patients. However there were highly significant differences (both at the .001 level) between staff responses and those from patients on active treatment and geriatric wards. We also found that admission ward patients differed significantly from both other patient groups, while the two longer stay wards did not differ from one another. In other words, the results paralleled those from the alienation study, in that the values of the admission ward patients are similar to those of the normal staff members, while the value of the long-stay patients are markedly different.

More specifically, we found that the longer a patient had been in hospital, the more important "physical" needs (eating, sleeping, exercise) became to him. The reverse was true for "social" needs (family, friends, and so on) which declined in importance with long hospitalization. "Abstract" goals in life (happiness, good life, success) also decreased in importance with long-stay patients.

SKILLS AND LENGTH OF HOSPITALIZATION

Studies of the skills and aptitudes of mental patients from the sociological viewpoint are rare in the literature. It is more common to credit a disinterest or lack of facility in an activity to physical impairment than to disuse. However, among our long-stay patients there are many skills that are used only infrequently in hospital. It is rhetorical to ask how many of our male patients have driven a car or tractor since they entered hospital. We performed a small study of cooking skills on a female geriatric ward,[16] and found that the women averaged twenty-one years since last cooking a full meal, eleven years since boiling an egg, nineteen years since baking a cake, and sixteen years since making soup. Many of the women were unfamiliar with new appliances and food prices. Of even more interest was that less than one-third of the women wanted to cook anything. Many expressed the feeling that they would not know how to cook or that they were satisfied with the present hospital food. In reading this paper, Dr. Richard Burrell made the point that self-contained wards, in which the patients perform all customary household activities, which would do much to prevent a loss of skills during prolonged hospitalization.

CHARACTERISTICS OF TWO GROUPS COMPARED

It is important from the standpoint of hospital strategy for the administrator to bear in mind the difference between these two groups of elderly patients. The one group is isolated, discultured, fitting easily into the hospital routine. The second group has interested relatives but is far more excitable, fragile, and discomfited by the hospital. To new patients, the hospital can be a frightening place —vast, impersonal, and over-crowded. The patient sleeps in a dormitory with forty elderly persons, eats in the dining room with a like number, and sits with them in an enormous dayroom. Privacy or a place for belongings is hard to come by. Most of the single and double bedrooms are already occupied by the tractable long-stay patients, who comprise the working force of the hospital. A study of hospital workers (100 per cent sample) showed that they average more than eighteen years in the hospital.

Considering the drastic change in milieu experienced by the newly admitted elderly patient, the mortality rate during the first five years is not surprising. When removed from their familiar environment, many animals become ill and die. Hediger mentions how after World War II a group of orphans was housed in a fine old castle.[17] Many types of psychological deficiency symptoms kept appearing until it was suggested to divide up the large areas into small rooms.

The long-stay elderly patient has had time to become accustomed to the hospital environment. In fact he may feel uncomfortable if placed in a small room or taken on a walk downtown. The newly admitted patient, however, has probably never lived in such a large area or been so close to so many people. It is interesting to note that this hospital is probably the largest structure within a 100-mile radius. We asked a random group of twenty-two patients (from all types of wards) whether they had ever been in a building as large as this hospital and, if so, whether they have stayed there for any length of time. We found only one patient, who had previously been in a mental hospital in another province, who had ever lived in as large a building, and only four patients had ever been inside as large a building. A few others who gave affirmative answers mentioned buildings that were decidedly smaller than this hospital. A conversation between the sick-ward physician and an elderly newly admitted patient may be illustrative. Upon being asked where he thought he was, the patient replied, "I don't know, it might be the Massey-Harris machine show, it's so big and so noisy."

In summary, we find decided differences between the two groups of elderly patients. Those who are recently admitted tend to maintain their contact with the outside through letters and visitors but are often unable to adjust to the unfamiliar hospital environment and may die shortly after admission. The long-stay patients, on the other hand, tend to lose contact with the outside in terms of letters and visitors and social values and skills but are well adjusted to the hospital milieu. This oversuccessful adjustment may in fact reduce the chances of the patient's leaving the hospital and living outside.

This study was supported by grants from the Rockefeller Foundation and the Department of Health and Welfare (Ottawa). Appreciation is expressed to Dr. H. Osmond, Mr. R. Hall, and Miss G. Whitney for their assistance in preparing this paper.

REFERENCES

1. HORBACZEWSKI, J.: Admissions of geriatric cases to a mental hospital. *Canad. Med. Ass. J., 78:*22-27, 1958.
2. MORGAN, N. C., AND JOHNSON, N. A.: Failures in psychiatry: The chronic hospital patient. *Amer. J. Psychiat, 113:*824-830, 1957.
3. SMITH, D.: *The Cross, 3:*Jan. 3, 1958.
4. BELKNAP. I.: *Human Problems of a State Mental Hospital.* New York, McGraw-Hill, 1956.
5. MOORE, W.: Institutionalitis. *Search,* p. 4, April—May 1958.
6. KRAMER, M., *et al.*: A historical study of the disposition of first admissions to a state mental hospital. Washington; U.S. Public Health Monograph No. 32, 1955.
7. MALZBERG, B.: Cohort studies of mental disease in New York State, 1943 to 1949. Part I. *Mental Hygiene, 40:*450-479, 1956.
8. LEOPOLD, N.: *Life Plus 99 Years.* New York, Doubleday, 1958.
9. ELKIN, W. A.: *The English Penal System.* Hormondsworth, England, Penguin Books, 1957.
10. JOHNSON, C. R.: *Prisoners of War.* Los Angeles, 1941.
11. CURLE, A.: Transitional communities and social reconnection. *Human Relations, 1:*42-68, 1947.
12. SOMMER, R.: Visitors to mental hospitals. *Mental Hygiene, 78:* 22-27, 1959.
13. SOMMER, R.: Letter-writing in a mental hospital. *Amer. J. Psychiat., 115:*514-517, 1958.
14. NETTLER, G.: A measure of alienation. *Amer. Soc. Rev, 22:*670-677, 1952.
15. SOMMER, R., AND HALL, R.: Alienation and mental illness. *Amer. Soc. Rev., 23:*418-420, 1958.
16. SOMMER, R.: Cooking skills of geriatric patients. *J. Amer. Geriatrics Soc.,* In press.
17. HEDIGER, H.: *Studies of the Psychology and Behavior of Animals in Zoos and Circuses.* New York, Criterion, 1955.

DISPLACED PERSONS: THE ELDERLY PATIENTS IN A LARGE MENTAL HOSPITAL*

Robert Sommer, Ph.D.

OF ALL THE ELDERLY PEOPLE in our culture, probably the ones whom we know least are those in our mental hospitals. They are indeed the forgotten ones—far removed from their homes and communities and often neglected by their own families. Many have grown old in the hospitals, spending some twenty to thirty years on the same ward. The hospital itself may have no definite program for its elderly patients. Perhaps the custodial care is satisfactory, but treatment and activity programs are directed toward the newly admitted younger patients. The nurses may resent being assigned to the geriatric wards "where nothing can be done." The elderly patient thus feels that he is an unwelcome guest at the hospital because the primary obligation of the hospital appears to lie elsewhere. Unfortunately, we know very little about the attitudes of elderly patients, especially those who have been removed from their communities for a decade or longer. At our hospital, we do know that very few receive mail or visitors.

This situation can be contrasted with that of the small community geriatric centers in the surrounding towns. There the patients receive and send letters, often entertain visitors, and eagerly read the daily papers. The men discuss politics and pride themselves in voting in all elections. The women crotchet and knit various articles for friends and relatives in the community. They have free access to a telephone, which they are encouraged to use. The various clubs and organizations in the community regularly

*Geriatrics, 13:653-661, October 1958.

visit the center and stage various programs for the patients. The residents of the centers are considered part of the local community, which is certainly not the case for the 1,500 residents at our mental hospital. Our patients and resident staff constitute a city in itself, but this is a far more impersonal and mobile community than the nearby town of 5,000 inhabitants.

OBJECTIVES OF THE STUDY

The administration of this hospital felt that it would be useful to determine the attitudes and feelings of our elderly patients. Very few of the psychiatrists spend any time on the geriatric wards, and the patients themselves are, on the whole, quite docile and accustomed to institutional life. In fact, we felt that some patients were not aware of a world outside the hospital doors.

Our first objective in making the study was twofold: to determine the patients' attitudes and feelings toward the hospital and to discover the extent of their contact with the world outside the hospital.

We felt that a questionnaire constructed along these lines could aid the social service staff in determining whether a patient was a good prospect for placement in a private home or geriatric center. This is an important problem as many mental hospitals have too few social workers, and these must be used to the greatest advantage. We assessed the patients' attitudes and feelings in four areas: 1) attitude toward the hospital, 2) attitude toward the outside, 3) ties to the outside, and 4) ties to the hospital.

The second objective of the study was to understand the psychologic needs of our geriatric patients. Previously we had to rely on impressionistic accounts by the staff and relatives. For example, many people maintained that the patients suffered because of their lack of privacy and the regimentation of life on the ward. A study of patient attitudes could help us to replace speculation and supposition with facts.

PROCEDURE

With the assistance of the social service and nursing departments, a large number of statements were collected that related to the patients' attitudes toward the hospital and the outside world.

These were then screened and edited. The resulting list was presented to the social service staff for their comments. Any item that was judged to be ambiguous or irrelevant was corrected or discarded. The items were then assembled into a four-page questionnaire which could be filled out by the patients or by the examiner in an interview. As the patients might not understand some of the items in a printed questionnaire, it was felt that an individual interview with each patient would be preferable.

Two geriatric wards in the hospital were selected for the study —a male ward with 105 patients and a female ward with thirty-seven patients. The average age of patients in each ward was sixty-nine years. Twenty patients from each ward were interviewed for the study. The only selection criteria were that they should be lucid and cooperative; otherwise they were taken at random. Interviews were conducted individually by a social worker or psychologist in a small room adjoining the ward's dayroom. If a patient were uncommunicative, delusional, or otherwise unable to be interviewed, another patient was selected.

After the scheduled twenty interviews on each ward were completed, the names of the twenty patients were typed on a list which was given to all nurses on the ward. The nurses were asked to indicate along a four-point scale whether the selected patients were good or poor risks for outside placement by the social service staff.

RESULTS

The final samples consisted of twenty men whose average age was sixty-five and who had spent an average of eleven years in a hospital and twenty women whose average age was seventy and who had spent an average of twenty-one years in the hospital. Fourteen other interviews had to be discarded because of incompleteness, delusions, or an inability to understand the items.

The actual questions and the patients responses are presented in Tables 1 to 4. As the responses of the men and women are almost identical, they were combined in these tables.

The question may arise as to whether the responses were honest and reasonable. In any survey, this can never be assumed. However, there are certain checks that can be built into a ques-

TABLE I
ATTITUDE TOWARD THE HOSPITAL

Query	Yes	No	Don't know
1. Do you like the food at the hospital?	26	11	3
2. Do you like the dances and parties at the hospital?	8	15	17
3. Do you have enough work to do here at the hospital?	32	6	2
4. Do you like the doctors at the hospital?	26	3	11
5. Do you like most of the nurses at the hospital?	39	1	0
6. In general, do you like the patients on your ward?	32	3	5
7. Are you able to be alone as much as you want here at the hospital?	29	10	1
8. Do they send you to bed too early at the hospital?	0	40	0
9. Do the nurses hurry you too much at meal time?	4	36	0
10. Do you feel lonely in the hospital?	21	19	0
11. Do you feel useful at the hospital?	23	12	5
12. Do you feel that they want you here at the hospital?	14	9	17
13. How many people sleep in your hospital room? Is this too many?	10	27	3
14. Do you dislike having your meals and going to bed at a set time?	4	34	2
15. Do you feel that you are a stranger at the hospital?	12	27	1
16. Are the nurses here kind to you?	35	2	3
17. Do you often feel bored at the hospital?	10	25	5
18. Can you move about the hospital as freely as you'd like?	30	8	2
19. Do the nurses here treat you like a child?	2	34	4
20. Do the nurses here understand you?	28	2	10
21. Would you like to be discharged from the hospital?	31	3	6

tionnaire. One of the simplest is to construct the items so that an equal number are pro and con. One can then see whether the respondents are indiscriminately agreeing with every item regardless of the content. In Tables 1 and 2, it can be seen that there were 738 positive responses and 674 negative responses to the opinion items. This would indicate that the patients were not simply agreeing to anything that was said by the interviewer. This is always a danger when the interviewing is done by an authority or high-status figure.

Another check is to see whether the responses within the groups are consistent and agree with known facts. In Table 1, item 8 shows that none of the forty patients felt that they are sent to bed too early. As there are very flexible bedtime hours on these wards, the responses accurately reflect reality. Item 2 discloses that only eight of the patients report that they like the dances and parties at the hospital. Since the recreational activities on these wards are sadly limited, this again is a reasonable response.

A third check is to see whether respondents are willing to answer in ways that will place themselves or authority figures

TABLE 2
ATTITUDE TOWARD THE OUTSIDE

Query	Yes	No	Don't know
1. Do you think that you'd get enough food of the kind you'd like if you lived outside?	35	1	4
2. Do you think that you'd have enough clothes of the kind you'd like if you lived outside?	36	0	4
3. Would you be alone as much as you wanted if you lived outside?	27	3	10
4. Would you like to travel and see other places?	17	21	2
5. Do you think that you would have enough money to live on if you left the hospital?	20	9	11
6. Would you object to living in a home that doesn't have running water and electricity?	14	22	4
7. Would it be difficult for you to get used to having your meals at a different time and going to bed at a different time than at the hospital?	4	28	8
8. Do you feel yourself a stranger to your family?	5	27	8
9. Do you feel yourself a stranger to your home town?	7	26	7
10. Are you needed or useful at home?	23	4	13
11. Do you feel that they want you at home?	14	3	23
12. Do you feel that you would be a bother to your family if you went home?	3	25	12
13. Are there a lot of stairs at home which would be difficult for you to climb?	2	21	17
14. Would you have enough to do if you lived outside the hospital?	31	0	9
15. Do you like the way your children have taken care of things while you've been away?	14	0	26
16. Do things move too fast on the outside?	10	23	7
17. Does shopping on the outside bother you?	4	31	5
18. Does traffic on the outside bother you?	4	34	2
19. Do you think that things on the outside have changed so much that it would be difficult for you to get along?	6	24	10
20. Do you think that you would like living with small children again?	15	18	7
21. Do you think that you would like living with people of the opposite sex again?	23	10	7
22. Do you think that people on the outside will look down on you because you've been a patient in a mental hospital?	8	17	15

in an unfavorable light. In Table 1, item 10 shows that 50 per cent of the patients feel lonely in the hospital. Item 1 shows that 28 per cent of the sample do not like the food at the hospital. Finally the interviewers themselves, all of whom were trained professional employees, were quite convinced of the sincerity of most of the responses. In cases in which a patient did not appear to understand an item, it was scored as "don't know" rather than pressing the patient for a reply. For simplicity in scoring, items that "did not apply" were scored as "don't know." Items in the various scales can be grouped under several heads: feelings about the hospital, present feelings, and feelings about the outside.

THE HOSPITAL

The patients were almost unanimous in their praise of the nurses. However, over a third of the patients complained that they rarely saw a doctor. Some sample responses from the female ward were: "I don't know any of them" and "I never had much experience with the doctors here." It can be noted that this is an open ward where the patients are given a large measure of responsibility. The staff had consciously attempted to spend as little time as possible on the ward in the hope that the women would gain an increased sense of responsibility.

PRESENT FEELINGS

More than half of the patients said that they felt lonely in the hospital. About 60 per cent of the men reported that they did not feel useful. Less than half of the patients felt that they were wanted at the hospital. At least one-fourth felt bored at the hospital, as if they were strangers, and also felt that they lacked sufficient privacy. It would be interesting to imagine how these would compare with the responses from patients in a community geriatric center. Certainly the number feeling "wanted" at the center would be far greater than at an institution which sees the treatment of young psychotic patients as its primary responsibility.

One rather striking conclusion from the questionnaire is that the patients did not object to the routine of the hospital. Few objected to having meals at designated hours, leaving the dining hall within a set time, or going to bed by 11 p.m. Apparently a set routine is not distasteful to these patients.

THE OUTSIDE

The feelings about the outside world were naive and overly optimistic. Few of the group envisaged any problems regarding money, food, recreation, or shelter if they were to leave the hospital. This is quite unrealistic and indicates their loss of contact with the outside. One particular patient parried the interviewer's question, "Do you think you would get enough food of the kind you'd like if you left the hospital?", with "The food is fine here." When asked, "Do you feel yourself a stranger to your home town?", he replied, "I can't tell you this. I am all right here." Some other patients were definite in their preference for living outside. Several men who had been in the hospital for a number of years maintained that they were needed on their farms and strongly desired to go home.

A majority of the patients had no desire to travel, to see other places, or to live with small children again. Whether these are characteristic of most older people or restricted to those living in institutions is something that we do not know.

TABLE 3
TIES TO THE HOSPITAL

Query	Yes	No	Don't know
1. Are you working here at the hospital?	27	13	0
2. Do you have a garden here at the hospital?	3	37	0
3. Do you go to the movies in the hospital?	8	32	0
4. Do you own any furniture on your ward?	1	37	2
5. Did you help buy any of the furniture on your ward?	0	37	3
6. Do you have any good friends on the . . . . . . (own sex) ward-? How many?.	20	17	3
7. Do you have any *good* friends on the . . . . . . (opposite sex) wards? How many?.	4	33	3
8. Do you take part in many hospital activities?	9	31	0
9. Do you have a group of friends here with whom you often get together and talk?	18	21	1
10. Do you receive a pension?	15	21	4
11. Do you receive other income?	10	23	7

TIES TO HOSPITAL

Approximately two-thirds of the group are working in the hospital. Activities are varied and include such tasks as sweeping, making beds, and work in the kitchen and laundry. Their recreational activities are more limited. Very few attend the films that are shown or take part in the parties and dances. One of the tragedies of large mental hospitals in isolated areas is that the staff is seldom able to establish a strong volunteer or visiting program. The nearest city of any size is seventy-five miles from our hospital. This is particularly unfortunate, as the patients do not have contact with anyone from the outside the institutions. Visitors are often able to serve as a bridge between hospital and community, while the staff, being identified with the institution, is not able to do so.

Only half of the patients report that they have any good friends on their own wards. This parallels our observations of the minimal social interaction on most of these wards. Patients are rarely seen talking together or engaged in any common activities. Although many people will look at TV in the evenings, this cannot be regarded as a socializing medium. In fact, social interaction usually comes to a standstill when the TV set is turned on.

A striking observation is that only 10 per cent of the patients have good friends among patients of the opposite sex and at least half of this 10 per cent consist of husbands who have wives in the hospital or mothers who have sons. Our geriatric wards are almost completely segregated as to sex even during recreation. A male patient may see no women except the nurses for some time.

TABLE 4
TIES TO THE OUTSIDE WORLD

Query	Yes	No	Don't know
1. Do you have a...... (husband or wife) living on the outside?	14	24	2
2. Do you have any children living on the outside?	21	19	0
3. Do you have any good friends living on the outside?	26	11	3
4. Do you belong to any lodge or organization?	5	31	4
5. Do you own a house?	15	23	2
6. Do you own any property?	18	20	2
7. Do you ever receive any letters from your relatives?	23	16	1
8. Did you receive any letters in the past month?	13	26	1
9. Do your relatives ever come to visit you?	19	21	0
10. Have they come in the past month?	5	35	0
11. Do you often read the newspapers?	28	12	0
12. Have you read a newspaper in the past week?	19	21	0

TIES TO THE OUTSIDE

Table 4 shows that one-third of the patients have husbands or wives living outside the hospital and that one-half have children living on the outside. About 40 percent of the patients say that they own a house or property. Nonetheless their contact with this outside world is far less than these items would indicate. Only one-quarter of the patients had received a letter during the preceding month, and about one-tenth had received visitors. These responses would indicate that patients do not lack *ties* to the outside but only contact with it.

During the month of November, a total of 945 letters were sent from all the wards of this 1,500-bed hospital. Although this figure is slightly inflated by inclusion of parcel receipts, acknowledgements, and so on, it still averages less than thirty-three letters per day for the entire hospital. It can be added that the patients on the admission wards usually send more letters than those on the geriatric ward. In one geriatric ward, one patient sent several letters each week, another sent about one a month, and a third had sent one letter since she was admitted to the ward about a year ago. That was the total for a ward of eighty-eight women. In contrast, when we visited community geriatric centers, we found almost every patient spending some part of the day writing letters to children or friends or even phoning former neighbors or friends in the community. This telephoning of friends *never* happens in our hospital. The nearest outside phone is almost inaccessible to the patients, and very few have friends in the nearby community.

The ward nurses were asked to rate each patient as a prospect for outside placement. The eleven nurses from each ward were given a list of the twenty patients from their ward who composed our sample, together with a four-point scale—excellent case, good case, fair case, and poor case—alongside each name. The average rating of each patient was computed and compared with the score on the questionnaire items. A pro-hospital score was derived by adding all items favorable to the hospital and subtracting those unfavorable. A pro-outside score was computed similarly, using the items on the second scale. The (product-moment) correlation between the nurses' rating of patient and his pro-hospital score was $.31 \pm .14$, which is statistically significant at the .05 level, indicating that patients who were favorably disposed toward the hospital tended to be rated as good candidates for discharge by the nurses. The (product-movement) correlation between the pro-outside score and the nurses' ratings was $-.18 \pm .15$, which is not statistically significant. A biserial correlation was run between the nurses. The (product- moment) correlation between the working in the hospital. This came out to be $.53 \pm .16$, which is significant beyond the .01 level. Although none of these correlations is very high, they showed that the nurses tended to rate as good candidates for discharge those patients who like the hospital, do not like the outside, and are working in the hospital.

DISCUSSION

These results show the disculturating effects of large isolated mental hospitals. Our patients are literally displaced persons. Not

only are they removed from friends and relatives, they are also in
an institution where they do not belong. Society must decide
whether it wants its mental hospitals to function as massive geriatric centers. If it does, then steps should be taken to provide recreational facilities and community contacts for these patients. Otherwise, as we have seen, these patients lose touch with friends and
children, and even with the flow of life on the outside. Few legislators would consider constructing a 1,000-bed geriatric center in
an isolated area, but this is what our mental hospital has become.

It is an apparent paradox that the new wonder drugs and
social therapies will do little toward solving this problem. Curing
the patient's illness or making him more tractable may not bring
him any closer to the community from which he came. Instead, the
mental hospital becomes filled with "well patients" who have an
extremely restricted choice of recreational or social activities. In
community centers, most of this is provided by townspeople and
service organizations, but this cannot be the case in isolated mental
hospitals.

On the basis of this survey, certain steps seem necessary within
the existing institutional framework. First, patients should be
strongly encouraged to send letters and cards as frequently as
possible. Letter writing should become a clearly defined and *expected* activity for patients on geriatric wards. This should yield
many dividends in terms of resuming past friendships and awak-
ening latent interests in both patients and relatives. It should help
to increase the number of visitors coming to the hospital, for
many of the visitors stop coming when they feel that the patients
are not really interested in seeing them.

Steps should be taken to correct the unisexual societies that
have been developed, and patients should be given an opportunity
to interact with both men and women. Interward teas and card
parties should be arranged and patient visiting encouraged. We
must emphasize that this should not be limited to the group of so-
called "better patients." Persons at various levels of social adjustment can profit from heterosexual contacts. The matter of increasing patients' contact with children or adolescents is more difficult to arrange. The director of a community geriatric center told
us how a boys' chorus had visited his institution and how much the

patients had appreciated it. If it is at all possible, we should arrange for our patients to at least *see* some children from time to time.

From the findings of the questionnaire, the social service staff feels that it has a better idea of the patients who are the best prospects for outside placement. This should enable the social workers to operate more effectively than under the previous policy or relying upon the recommendations of the nursing staff. On the basis of the questionnaire responses, the patient group has been classified along a continuum ranging from strongly pro-hospital and anti-outside to strongly anti-hopsital and pro-outside. The first group consists of the well-institutionalized patients who are primarily a problem for the nursing and recreation staffs. Members of the second group are well motivated for discharge, but one should carefully examine their objections to the hospital environment to see that these same factors are not present in the homes in which they are placed. Probably the best prospects for the social workers are those patients who are strongly pro-outside and moderately pro-hospital. Patients who are both strongly pro-hospital and strongly pro-outside are placed easily on the outside, but their return rate is higher than patients who are less favorably disposed toward the hospital.

The nursing staff should revise its thinking as to the types of patients who are best candidates for discharge. Too often the nurses consider the well-institutionalized, steady worker as the best candidate for discharge. This patient may become so well adjusted to the hospital society that he cannot adjust outside the hospital grounds. The nurses must be taught that it is not sufficient for a patient to adjust to the hospital routine but that he must be encouraged to resume and maintain his contact with the outside world.

The rating scale on which the nurses indicated the patient's suitability for discharge proved to be an interesting instrument in its own right, for it tended to focus the attention of the nurses on rehabilitation to life on the outside. The social workers felt that this rating scale was of little use to them at present and that there was need for greater liaison between social workers and nurses as to their respective goals. The nurses had only a hazy idea of their role in the total treatment plan of the hospital and were not fully aware of the need for getting the patient *beyond* the point of good hospital adjustment. Use of even a simple rating scale should help to focus their attention on this last step.

THE FAMILY PHYSICIAN, THE COMMUNITY, AND THE AGED*

William F. Sheeley, M.D.

Perhaps we are mistaken in seeing the problem posed by our older people as primarily one of numbers—numbers of persons who will have to be supported in their helpless dotage. Because we have assumed that people over sixty-five must surely disintegrate mentally and physically and therefore become dependent socially and economically, we have aspired to do little more than provide for their creature needs—more and more beds in state mental hospitals, in old folk's homes and in other custodial establishments.

However, many physicians are beginning to ask with greater insistence whether the high dependency, morbidity, and mortality among our older people are inevitable concomitants of advancing age; whether people are being forced prematurely to abandon economically useful activity, social relations with their fellow men, and participation in community affairs; whether many old people's nutritional and degenerative disorders could not be alleviated or even obviated; and whether community disinterest in the old person does not more often cause depression and confusion than does senile brain changes.

If these doubters are right—if we can correct and avoid many of the accepted attributes of old age—then solving the problem of properly managing the old person is not simple at all. Solutions will require complex and coordinated social action, such as programs to change community attitudes toward the aged and to provide economic, social, medical, and psychiatric assistance.

*Geriatrics, 16:321-327, July 1961.

CURRENT IDEAS ABOUT AGING

Let us examine a few instances of the current attitudes, policies, and practices that students of the aging process are beginning to question:

Public Attitude May Accelerate Aging. One important attitude is our pessimistic view of the elderly person, which may favor his desuetude and death. Thinking we can do little more than house him, we seek to house him cheaply among large aggregations of older people. We are sending more old people to state mental hospitals that may have a daily census of more than 10,000. Swallowed up by these hundreds and thousands, the aged person soon loses his remaining sense of personal identity. The result is mental confusion, poor appetite, nutritional disorders, dehydration, and electrolyte disturbances; the aged person sickens and takes to his bed, circulatory embarrassment and pneumonia develop, and he dies. Obviously, some older people have psychiatric illness and these people can benefit as much as younger ones from active psychiatric therapy.

The old person sent, not to a state hospital, but a good nursing home is more apt to preserve a sense of identity, but even there he faces an assumption of inexorability. Those who care for him assume he will leave only by dying. Such loss of future encourages in the old person feelings of rejection, hopelessness, and depression. Still another old person, kept at home, may find himself in a hostile family amid a custodial, waiting-for-death atmosphere.

The elderly person who escapes state hospital, rest home, and hostile family may still be discouraged from active participation in the community. When he tries to get a new job performing tasks at which he is skilled, he is told that he is too old to be hired; when he already has such a job, he is told on some anniversary of his birth that he must retire. Both employers and labor union leaders try to lower the retirement age.

The community gives little more socially than economically. For social stimulation, the old person must look to others quite as on the shelf and stripped of prestige as he. Denying him all social participation, the community may send him to a distant monastic retreat that is pleasant and serene but very dull and enervating.

Physicians Are Unrealistically Pessimistic. Too often, the family physician shares the general pessimism. When he sees a bedridden, incontinent, confused, slightly feverish person, he rarely sets as his therapeutic goal the restoration of this man to his part-time job in the canning factory or the return of this woman to caring for her husband and home. He considers these phenomena of senility the endpoint of an irreversible physical disintegration.

This medical pessimism may explain the relatively limited enthusiasm for practice or research in geriatrics and gerontology. Enthusiasm has been growing lately, although the responsibility for treating disorders of old age is often scattered among all the branches and subbranches of medicine, where it often gets short shrift. A specialist tends toward greater interest in younger persons, since disorders in older people affect such a variety of organ systems that he cannot extricate those of peculiar interest to his specialty.

Research into the causes and nature of aging tends to be as fragmented and sketchy as the therapy. Although an old age project is under way here and there, a national study program of broad scope commensurate with the problem just does not exist. Behind the lethargy and inactivity lies the question: "Is it worthwhile to invest a lot of thought, energy resources, and money in people who are soon to be dead?"

FALLACY OF THE INEXORABLE AGING PROCESS

What evidence supports the more optimistic, if somewhat unsettling, presumption that many babbling persons can be restored to a measure of social usefulness, personal clarity, and happiness?

Independent People Age More Slowly. It is frequently observed that old persons who refuse to become excessively dependent and instead live self-sufficiently seem to retain their physical and mental vigor longer than their less aggressive contemporaries. True, the cause-effect relationship may be quite the opposite: some oldsters may stay active longer because they luckily have good physical and mental health.

This is a proper question for scientific investigation. Until we have contrary evidence, however, we can accept the hypothesis that people who remain active in a gratifying and socially useful way are able to maintain adequate mental and physical "tone." Physicians themselves, for instance, frequently continue in active medical practice well into their seventies or eighties. People in other occupations not having obligatory retirement, as in professional writing, often make useful social contributions far beyond age sixty-five. Titian painted when well past ninety despite fingers so crippled he had to tie the brush to his wrist. Those forced to retire from gainful work, but who are able to find a demanding and rewarding avocation, often live on with happy vigor long after their former co-workers have fallen into atrophic heaps by the fire. The housewife who must bustle to meet the demands of a retired husband often survives him many years.

Physical Disorders Are Often Reversible. It has long been known that older people are more susceptible than younger ones to injury and disease and tend to be more prostrated by these traumata, and that they recover more slowly. The mentally clear old man who is forced by a minor surgical procedure to lie quietly in bed for a few days may suffer far-reaching neurologic effects because of attendant slowing of cerebral blood flow, general dehydration, and electrolyte imbalance. Another old man with little memory loss or orientation difficulty in the comparatively simple environment of his home town may become quite confused and forgetful during a visit to a married daughter who lives near the busy avenue of a large city. In the old widow living alone, who is not inspired to prepare tasty and nutritious meals, alarming degrees of nutritional anemia, deficiencies of important elements of the blood chemistry, and other sequelae of dietary defect may develop insidiously.

What has not been so widely known, however, is that although these conditions occur quickly and subside slowly, they often can be largely reversed by comprehensive diagnosis and through treatment. The physician's exquisitely detailed diagnostic study will uncover a plethora of small and correctible discrepancies. The individual discrepancies may not be particularly exciting and, in a younger person, they might properly be ignored. In the older person, however, each must be carefully and painstakingly corrected so far as possible. One makes therapeutic progress, then, on a broad front of many little manipulations rather than in a dramatic breakthrough.

Psychiatric Illness Is Often Reversible. Psychiatric disorders associated with old age show a similar gratifying reversibility even with massive brain damage. Although most people have considered the symptoms of senility—the short memory span, disorientation, difficulties with abstract thinking, and so on—to be the direct result of brain damage, neurologists and others have also seen that the severity of symptoms may correlate very little with the amount of brain damage found at autopsy. Thus, the spry old person, clear-headed until the final coma, may have many areas of brain damage, whereas the dodering old person may have a surprisingly intact brain. Here, too, questions are raised that will be confidently answered only after much research has been completed. Failure to correlate amount of behavior change with quantity of brain damage may be unimportant. The quality of brain damage, or the effect on neurophysiologic processes in the affected area, may really determine behavioral disturbance.

Even if foci of brain damage do produce specific psychiatric symptoms, however, we cannot gainsay the effect of the psychosocial environment on the old person. We must look beyond the brain damage to explain fully the causes of the senile syndrome, and we must use both somatic and psychosocial therapies to treat it. For example, the greatly increased incidence of suicide during the sixth, seventh, and eighth decades of life reflects the increasing prevalence of depression; such depression is so common that we risk taking it for granted and therefore either failing entirely to note it or correct it.

Depression can be treated, however, by a holistic approach that exploits social, psychologic, and somatic therapies. Often, the physician needs to do little more than encourage his aged patient from visit to visit and to ask him for a brief listing of his current problems and emotional reactions to them. Other times, he may also ask a psychiatrist to give electroshock or antidepressant drug therapies. Further, he may ease much of the painful anxiety of old age by giving low doses of ataractic and and other psychiatric drugs. And, of course, the family physician can help to create more healthful psychologic and social attitudes within the older person himself and among members of his family and community. All these maneuvers can reverse the psychiatric disorder progressively crippling the patient.

APPLICATION OF NEW PRINCIPLES

These general and abstract principles can be applied in many possible ways.

Physician Leads Acceptance of Old Person. If families can be shown how to bring the older person pleasantly into many family activities, while respecting his need for privacy and their own, they can enrich their lives and his and free themselves of the feeling of unfulfilled obligation so often stultifying to such relationships. The old person's economic contribution to the family can range from household chores, such as baby-sitting and housework, to part-time jobs in the community to help pay the rent.

Clubs and churches can profitably use the old person's skills, experience and judgment, and available leisure time. By calling upon him for help, they give him a sense of being needed and also free younger members for other club duties. Older people can be used even more than they are as volunteer workers in state mental hospitals and for fund-raising drives of charitable organizations and institutions. To assist community projects, old persons can make satisfying contributions that range from giving advice based on their professional or civic experience to implementing selected aspects of community policies.

An economic rehabilitation program for old people can have many values. The physician can encourage study of the over-all job requirements of the community. Perhaps he can induce the state department of vocational rehabilitation to list part-time jobs and other relatively low-demand jobs which are either not being performed or are being performed by younger persons having greater economic usefulness in more demanding work. Once such jobs are found, it may be necessary to convince employers that an overage person can profitably and safely fill them. Employers liability laws may have to be modified and appropriate waivers of responsibility provided. One may have to assuage the apprenhension of labor unions, which fear hiring old people will cause unemployment of younger heads of families. When these obstacles have been overcome, a job-placement service—a sort of employment agency for older people—can be created to fit man and job to one another.

Physicians De-emphasize State Hospitalization. Physicians should also help move the primary locale of therapy for somatically ill and confused oldsters from the state mental hospital into the home community. The state mental hospital is not ideal for managing aged persons who are not psychiatrically ill. For one thing, their economy-ridden budgets are much too low to provide bedfast patients with the vital treatment so expensive in professional time and in medical supplies and equipment. State hospitals have far too little staff to do the medical and nursing job properly; these staff shortages include not only doctors and nurses but also nurses aides, janitors, and laundry personnel. Furthermore, because of overcrowding, ward units produce a mélange of wandering people and feeling of confusion and formlessness. Such a shifting milieu is most unsuitable for the old patient.

A Community Complex for Geriatric Problems. Suitable management of the aged person can be provided by a complex of general hospital, nursing homes, and community social agencies. The basic units of such a complex are 1) a geriatric ward or at least a geriatric service in a local general hospital, 2) rest and nursing homes, and 3) community social agencies with departments or offices staffed to deal with problems of old people. Among them, these three units provide 1) definite and comprehensive diagnostic and therapeutic care for the very sick old person, 2) convalescent care and temporary haven for the less debilitated patient, and 3) social and economic assistance for the physically able person needing to effect better relations with his family, clubs, and community and to reestablish himself economically. Naturally, the component units of this complex must function in a tight system of coordination and collaboration.

Under such a system, a given patient might be brought into the geriatric service of the general hospital in a state of profound physical debilitation and mental disintegration. A corrective medical, including psychiatric, regimen would be quickly started after complete diagnostic study and recommendation by several specialist-consultants. After recovering somewhat, he would be moved

to a nursing home but seen at appropriate intervals by the hospital
staff either in the home or in the hospital's clinic. On the one or
two occasions when his condition worsened, he would be returned
temporarily to the hospital.

Finally, having achieved enduring mental and physical improvement, he would be moved to a rest home. There he would
be interviewed by a member of the vocational rehabilitation
agency to determine his job interests and capabilities; family problems arising from his illness would be worked out with the assistance of community social agencies.

About this time, he would find a job giving considerable economic self-sufficiency. After meeting in the rest home and enjoying the
company of a man with similar physical and economic conditions,
he might move with the other man into living arrangements suitable to their age and incomes. A social agency would help them find
their new home and continue to provide the minimal supervision
necessary to safeguard them in case of misadventure.

This story perhaps idealizes the results such a management
complex might achieve, but the principles involved are nonetheless hard-headed and practical. If patients in rest and nursing
homes had close medical supervision to detect disorders early, had
prompt hospitalization and as much treatment as possible in the
nursing home, not only human lives but a good deal of money
would be saved. Furthermore, even patients who never recover
sufficiently to move out of the nursing home would see others go
home and profit from the morale-building hope that they themselves might one day move on into the community.

The hospital can operate geriatric clinics both for patients
in rest and nursing homes and for those who might be prevented
by the clinic from ever needing such domiciliary care. To treat
these patients, clinics can exploit the support afforded by sister
medical, surgical, and psychiatric clinics. They can also be closely
associated with the state hospital system. The board and standard
operating policies of such connections with the state hospital
should be worked out at the outset by negotiation with the state
mental health program director.

Once these policies have been formulated, conditions of closest
possible collaboration should be established between staffs of the

respective clinic and state hospital. The clinic can function both as a screen to prevent avoidable commitment to the state hospital and as a follow-up facility to reduce the number of readmissions. Finally, the clinic can have close ties not only with the state hospital system but also with all community social agencies concerned with welfare of the elderly. Potentially, clinics and social agencies can provide great mutual assistance.

Gerontology Requires More Emphasis in Medical Schools. Meanwhile, the family physician can encourage medical schools to place greater emphasis at both undergraduate levels on the care of aged people. Perhaps this emphasis could be accomplished if every department of the medical school stress optimistic treatment of the older patient. Interspecialty collaboration would underscore the interrelated way in which many concurrent organ system disorders occur. Several departments together could point out the hazards to which old people are susceptible, the important danger signals, and the corrective measures to be taken.

Postgraduate Education Increases Skill of Practicing Physicians. Education in treating older persons should not stop at the graduate level, however; great potential value lies in the postgraduate education of the practicing physician—the general practitioner, the internist, the surgeon, the psychiatrist—whose job is made easier and more successful when he applies sophisticated medical management technics to the older patient. One problem is that comparatively few postgraduate courses are being specifically offered to increase the physician's skill in geriatrics. Although some useful information is given in the occasional lecture in a multisubject seminar or scientific meeting, the number and duration of these courses could be considerably expanded. Also, some courses should be devoted exclusively to gerontology and geriatrics.

EDUCATION IN PSYCHIATRIC GERONTOLOGY

As a psychiatrist, I am perhaps especially sensitive to the need for courses in what might be called psychiatric gerontology, because I believe many of the deficiencies in management arise in part from unfamiliarity with psychiatric principles. Since the problem of geriatric care is so comprehensive and requires such a broad approach, it may well be that the family physician with psychiatric understanding is best suited to assume primary responsibility for these older patients. He would, of course, have close consultive support of such specialists as the psychiatrist. The psychiatrist is responsible for transmitting to him the understanding and skill required for effective management of emotional problems among the elderly.

Medical Organizations Can Sponsor Postgraduate Education. Medical organizations in every state are responsible for seeing that postgraduate psychiatric training is offered to nonpsychiatrist physicians. Among these organizations are 1) mental health committees of state and local medical societies, 2) district branches of the American Psychiatric Association, 3) mental health committees of state and local units of the American Academy of General Practice, 4) departments of psychiatry in medical schools and teaching hospitals, 5) state departments or divisions of mental health and appurtenant state hospitals, and 6) other public and private mental hospitals.

This incomplete list illustrates potential resources to which the interested physician can turn for training. In many parts of the country, two or more state and local organizations unite to plan and present psychiatric courses. Although these courses usually are concerned with psychiatric problems affecting both young and old persons, their faculties constitute a cadre about which to assemble other courses on psychiatric management of the older person.

Family Physicians Admit Geriatric Patients to Psychiatric Wards. After participating in such a psychiatric course—or perhaps as a less desirable substitute for such participation—the physician can get direct psychiatric consultation as he manages selected psychiatric problems among the aged. In a few places in the United States and Canada, an idea which has excited some interest is being tried tentatively: nonpsychiatrist physicians are admitting their patients to the psychiatric wards of general hospitals and are then continuing to exercise a measure of responsibility for their care. The amount of responsibility is determined from time to time by repeated conferences between the attending physician and the chief of the psychiatric service. Such responsibility is based on the severity and nature of the patient's psychiatric disorder and on the physician's level of psychiatric experience and competence. Obviously, the physician who has participated in courses offered by the psychiatric staff and has worked with the staff will be better known to them and therefore be given greater amounts of responsibility. This arrangement expands available psychiatric care in the hospital on the one hand and enhances the psychiatric skills of staff physicians on the other.